The Dog Next Door

AND OTHER STORIES

THEODORE CLYMER · PATRICIA MILES MARTIN

CONSULTANTS

ROGER W. SHUY · E. PAUL TORRANCE
LINGUISTICS   CREATIVITY

GINN AND COMPANY
A XEROX COMPANY

Acknowledgments

Grateful acknowledgment is made to the following authors and publishers for permission to use and adapt copyrighted materials:

Atheneum Publishers for the adaptation of "Chipmunk Goes Hunting" by Eleanor Clymer. Copyright © 1965 by Eleanor Clymer. From *Chipmunk in the Forest.* Used by permission of Atheneum Publishers.

Doubleday & Company, Inc., for the poem "Mice," copyright 1932 by Doubleday & Company, Inc., from *Fifty-One New Nursery Rhymes* by Rose Fyleman. Reprinted by permission of Doubleday & Company, Inc.

Golden Press, Inc., for "Crispin's Crispian," originally published as "Mr. Dog, the Dog Who Belonged to Himself" by Margaret Wise Brown. Reprinted as an adaptation by permission from *A Treasury of Little Golden Books* edited by Ellen Lewis Buell. © Copyright 1960 by Golden Press, Inc.

Harcourt Brace Jovanovich, Inc., for "The Bear Says North." Copyright, 1922, by Parker Fillmore, renewed, 1950, by Louise Fillmore. Reprinted from *The Shepherd's Nosegay* by Parker Fillmore edited by Katherine Love, by permission of Harcourt Brace Jovanovich, Inc.; and for the poem "If You Find a Little Feather," from *Something Special,* © 1958, by Beatrice Schenk de Regniers. Reprinted by permission of Harcourt Brace Jovanovich, Inc.

Little, Brown and Company for "Fox and the Fire," adapted, with selected illustrations, from *Fox and the Fire* by Miska Miles, illus-trated by John Schoenherr. Text Copyright © 1966 by Miska Miles. Illustrations Copyright © 1966 by John Schoenherr. Both by permission of Atlantic-Little, Brown and Co., and for the poem "Song of the Train," from *Far and Few* by David McCord. Copyright 1952 by David McCord. By permission of Little, Brown and Co.

W. W. Norton & Company, Inc., for the poem "Sudden Storm" by Elizabeth Coatsworth. Reprinted from *The Sparrow Bush,* rhymes by Elizabeth Coatsworth. By permission of W. W. Norton & Company, Inc. Copyright © 1966 by W. W. Norton & Company, Inc.

G. P. Putnam's Sons for "No, No, Rosina," adapted from *No, No, Rosina* by Patricia Miles Martin. Copyright © 1964 by Patricia Miles Martin; and for "The Raccoon and Mrs. McGinnis," adapted from *The Raccoon and Mrs. McGinnis* by Patricia Miles Martin. Copyright © 1961 by Patricia Miles Martin. Both used and adapted by permission of G. P. Putnam's Sons.

The Viking Press, Inc., for the poem "Yucca," from *In My Mother's House* by Ann Nolan Clark. Copyright 1941 by Ann Nolan Clark. Reprinted by permission of The Viking Press, Inc.

The World Publishing Company for the adaptation of "Here We Go" by Maria Leach. Adapted by permission of The World Publishing

Company from *The Thing at the Foot of the Bed and Other Scary Stories* by Maria Leach. Copyright ⓒ 1959 by Maria Leach.

Anne Alexander, for her story "Grand Canyon National Park."

Wm. Collins Sons & Co. Ltd., for the poem "If You Find a Little Feather," from *Something Special* by Beatrice Schenk de Regniers. Reprinted by permission of Wm. Collins Sons & Co. Ltd.

Gladys Y. Cretan, for her story "The Clover Street Trio."

Dover Publications, Inc., for the poem "The Purple Cow," from *The Purple Cow and Other Nonsense* by Gelett Burgess.

Berniece Freschet, for her stories "The Beavers Build a House" and "Little Pronghorn."

Kathryn D. Henderson for "Down the Mississippi," adapted from *Augustus and the River* by LeGrand Henderson. Copyright ⓒ 1939 by LeGrand Henderson. Copyright renewed. Adapted by permission of McIntosh and Otis, Inc.

J. B. Lippincott Company for "The Mouse Who Liked to Read in Bed." Adapted from *The Mouse Who Liked to Read in Bed* by Miriam Clark Potter. Copyright ⓒ 1958 by Miriam Clark Potter. Published by J. B. Lippincott Company; for the poem "Mrs. Peck-Pigeon" from *Poems for Children* by Eleanor Farjeon. Copyright, 1933, 1961 by Eleanor Farjeon. Published by J. B. Lippincott Com-

pany; and for the poem "The Goblin" from *Picture Rhymes from Foreign Lands* by Rose Fyleman. Copyright 1935, 1963 by Rose Fyleman. Published by J. B. Lippincott Company.

Lothrop, Lee & Shepard Co., Inc., for the adaptation of "Sylvester Jones and the Voice in the Forest" by Patricia Miles Martin. By permission of Lothrop, Lee & Shepard Co., Inc., from *Sylvester Jones and the Voice in the Forest* by Patricia Miles Martin, copyright 1958, by Lothrop, Lee & Shepard Co., Inc.

Harold Ober Associates Inc., for the poem "Mrs. Peck-Pigeon," from *Poems for Children* by Eleanor Farjeon. Copyright ⓒ 1951 by Eleanor Farjeon. Reprinted by permission of Harold Ober Associates Inc.

Rand McNally & Company for the abridgment of "Puddlejumper" by Dorothea Snow. Abridged from *Puddlejumper*, by Dorothea Snow, copyright 1948 by Rand McNally & Company.

The Society of Authors for the poem "The Goblin," from *Picture Rhymes from Foreign Lands* by Rose Fyleman; and for the poem "Mice," from *Fifty-One New Nursery Rhymes* by Rose Fyleman. Both reprinted by permission of The Society of Authors as the literary representative of the Estate of the late Rose Fyleman.

Contents

1

THE DOC NEXT DOOR

7

The Bradleys Move In →

William and Lucy Brown sat
on their steps, watching a big van.

The van was coming along the street.
It stopped at the house next door.
A woman was waiting there in the doorway.

New people were going to move in. Someone
was coming to live in the house next door.

8

Two men began to take a big basket
out of the moving van.

"Put that big basket over there, please,"
the woman said. "That's fine."

William was thinking about the new people.
He hoped there would be a boy in the family.

"I hope a girl moves in there," Lucy said.
Lucy's big cat was sitting on her lap.

"I'm going over there and ask if there is a boy
in the family," William said. "You stay here, Lucy."
But Lucy followed him.

The moving men were going up the front walk with a big box.

"You can take that box to the back door," the woman said.

The men took the box and William waited by the front door till the woman looked at him and smiled.

"Hello," she said. "Do you live around here?"

"Yes. I live next door. I'm William Brown."

"I'm Mrs. Bradley. Stanley will be pleased to have a boy next door."

William was happy.

"There's a BOY in the family," he thought.

10

Mrs. Bradley was still talking.
"Mr. Bradley and Stanley will be coming
very soon."

Along the street came a little car
with a man in it. A great big dog
sat beside him. The car stopped
in front of the house and the dog barked
and jumped out.

WOOF
WOOF

"THAT'S Stanley?" William said.
"Stanley is a DOG?"

Stanley was barking as he came up the walk.
Everyone could see that Stanley was very happy.
And everyone could see that Lucy's cat
and William were not happy at all.

The cat jumped down and climbed into an oak tree.
When Stanley barked, the cat climbed higher.

The moving men came up the walk
with a big doghouse.

Stanley was still barking,
and the cat climbed still higher.
Up she went—higher—still higher—

"Someone will have to get that cat
down from the tree," Mr. Bradley said.

"The cat will come down," Lucy said.
"She knows about that oak tree."

The moving men looked at Mrs. Bradley.
"We are almost finished. Everything is
in the house but this. Where does it go?"

"Move the doghouse back by the fence, please,"
Mrs. Bradley said.

Stanley followed them around back.
Lucy's cat came down from the oak tree
and ran home.

When the men came back, Stanley came too,
and jumped up on William.

"Say, Mrs. Bradley," William said.
"Would it be all right if I take Stanley
for a walk?"

"Stanley would like that very much,"
Mrs. Bradley said.

William and Stanley and Lucy went
down the street.

"This is where OUR family lives, Stanley,"
Lucy said. "We live here with our mother
and father. And the cat that climbed
up in your oak tree was MY cat.
You and the cat have to be friends."

"Stanley doesn't know about talk,"
William said.

"How do you know?" Lucy asked.

William didn't know how to answer.
He thought about this for a long time.

14

Stanley was having a good time.
Every now and then he ran away, looking
in people's gardens. But each time,
he came right back and walked beside William.
William was feeling better now, but he
still wished that a boy had moved next door.

"This is a nice dog," Lucy said. "It's
almost as good as having a girl next door."

"It's not almost as good as having a girl
next door," William said. "It's better."

Green Paint

Lucy Brown's father was painting the patio
at the side of the house.

Lucy was standing by the gate with her cat.
Lucy's brother was tossing a baseball into the air.

Their father was painting the patio green.
He had almost finished his work.

"This job is almost finished," he said.

16

Lucy climbed up on the gate to get
a better look at the patio.

"Keep that cat out of here, Lucy,"
her father said. He swished his brush around.
"And you stay out too. I don't want people
coming in here and walking on the wet paint."

He swished his brush around again. "I think
I would like to put a sign out there. William
had better make a sign while I finish painting.
Make a KEEP OUT sign, William, so people
will stay out while this paint is still wet."

"Why don't I make the sign
while you paint?" Lucy asked.

"You can't spell," William said.

"You can tell me how," said Lucy.

"Help her, William," their father said.
"Put the sign out there on the gate
before someone comes."

William and Lucy hurried into the house.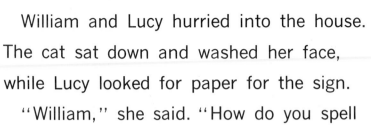
The cat sat down and washed her face,
while Lucy looked for paper for the sign.

"William," she said. "How do you spell
KEEP OUT ?"

"C-O-M-E I-N," William said.

After Lucy finished the sign,
William looked at it and smiled.
The letters were big and black.

Lucy hurried outside. "No one will come
in here after I get my sign up," she thought,
as she put the sign on the gate. The sign said:

18

Come In

After a while Mrs. Bradley from next door
came over with her dog Stanley.

"What a nice sign," Mrs. Bradley said.

"I think I have to go now," said William,
as he hurried around to the back of the house.

After William left, Mrs. Bradley looked
at the sign again. Then she and Stanley
went inside.

"Watch out there, Mrs. Bradley,"
Mr. Brown said. "Didn't you see the sign?"

"Why yes," Mrs. Bradley said. "I saw it.
It says COME IN."

"Lucy," Mr. Brown said. "Did you make
that sign?"

"Yes, I did," Lucy said. "I thought it said
KEEP OUT."

"William," Mr. Brown called. "William!
Come back here!"

William hurried back.

"William. Get in here and paint this over.
Here's the brush. RIGHT NOW."

"Do you want him to paint over
Stanley's paw prints too?" Lucy asked.

"YES," her father said. "Paw prints too!"
William swished the brush around.

20

Lucy looked at the patio. She knew
she would always remember the green paint.
She knew she would always remember Stanley's
big paw prints running all over the green patio.

She looked at William. She knew that William
would always remember too. He was swishing
his brush around, flipping paint
here and there and everywhere.

21

Everyone knew that William was happy.
"Wait, William," Lucy said. She called
to her father. "Can we have just ONE
of Stanley's paw prints in the paint?"
"Well . . . all right," her father said.
"We will keep one. Just one paw print."

Lucy and her father and Mrs. Bradley
watched William, who was still painting.
And they all knew, that after he finished,
there would always be one big paw print
on the green patio.

It Looks Like Rain

"William," Mrs. Brown said.
"I want you to put your raincoat on
when you go to school today.
It looks like rain."

She looked at Lucy. This was Lucy's
first week of school. "And Lucy,
I want you to put your raincoat on too."

"I don't need a raincoat," Lucy said.
"I can take my umbrella."

"Put your raincoat on and take your umbrella
too," their mother said.

23

William went to get the raincoats
and an umbrella.

Lucy put on her raincoat. She looked
at the umbrella.

"This is the old one," she said.
"It has holes in it and rain comes right through.
I'll get all wet when the rain comes through."

Lucy liked having an umbrella to carry
in the rain, but she didn't want to carry one
with holes that would let the rain through.
She went to find her new one.

24

When William and Lucy opened the front door,
Stanley, the dog next door, was waiting.
He decided that he would walk to school
with William and Lucy.

Stanley jumped around, wanting to carry
something. William decided to let him carry
his book bag.

Stanley went off carrying it proudly.
Proudly, Lucy walked with him,
carrying the new umbrella. She wished
it would rain so she could open it.

When they got to school, Stanley put
the book bag on the steps and went back home.

All through the day Lucy wished for rain.

When it was time to go home from school,
Miss Little said, "Don't forget to put on
your raincoats, and don't forget to take
your umbrellas. There is a gray cloud
in the sky and it looks like rain."

Outside, Lucy looked up at the sky.
The sky was blue-gray. There was a big gray cloud
up there, but it wasn't raining.

Then Lucy looked down the street
and saw Stanley coming to meet her.
He jumped around, wanting to carry something.
"I don't have a thing that you can carry
but my umbrella," Lucy said.
Stanley was still jumping.
Lucy decided to let him carry
her new umbrella.
"All right, Stanley," she said.
"Stop jumping. Here. Take it."
Proudly, Stanley took the umbrella.

Lucy and Stanley started home.
When they were almost home, it started to rain.

"Let me have my umbrella," Lucy said to Stanley.
Stanley backed away.

Lucy started to take the umbrella from Stanley,
but Stanley tugged at it.

"DROP IT," Lucy said. "DROP IT."

Lucy knew that Stanley was not going to drop it.

Lucy's friends were coming along the street.
They all had their umbrellas open but Lucy.
At last Jane Ann came along.

"You can walk under MY umbrella," she said.
"Two of us can fit under it."

They started down the street. Stanley
trotted along, carrying Lucy's umbrella.

The next morning Lucy went outside to look
at the sky. There was a gray cloud up there,
a very big gray cloud. She decided
that it looked like rain.

Stanley was waiting on the walk.

"I'll have to take my umbrella to school,"
Lucy said to her mother.

"And don't forget to put your raincoat on,"
her mother said.

"I won't forget." Lucy picked up two umbrellas—
her own new one, and the old one.

"What are you going to do with that old umbrella?"
William asked.

"I have decided to let Stanley have it," she said.
"He can have the old umbrella for his own—
his very own!"

29

They started down the street.

Proudly, Stanley was carrying his own old umbrella.

When they were almost there, it started to rain.

Lucy opened her own new umbrella.

She listened to the drops of rain
on her umbrella.

She listened to the swish—swish—swish of water
when cars went by.

She listened to friends calling to each other.

It was a fine morning.

She and William hurried on to school.

30

Sudden Storm

The rain comes in sheets
Sweeping the streets,
Here, here, and here,
Umbrellas appear,
Red, blue, yellow, green,
They tilt and they lean
Like mushrooms, like flowers
That grow when it showers.

Elizabeth Coatsworth

William Gets His Hair Cut

William Brown needed to have his hair cut.

"If you don't get your hair cut pretty soon, it will be as long as mine," Lucy said.

William didn't answer.

"Here is money to get your hair cut," his father said. "If you hurry back home, I will take you to the baseball game today."

William decided to hurry.

He wanted to go to the game.

William got on his bicycle and started
down the street to go to the barber shop.
Lucy was calling Stanley, the dog next door,
but Stanley decided to follow William's bicycle.

William parked his bicycle outside
the barber shop. Stanley began to push
into the shop ahead of William.

"You stay outside," William said.

He went inside and sat down to wait.
There were four men ahead of him.

William could see Stanley through the window.
Stanley wanted to find another way
to get inside the barber shop. He went
into the hat shop next door.

Pretty soon Stanley came rushing out.
A woman was running after him.

She looked in the window of the barber shop
and then opened the door.

"Where did that big dog come from?" she asked.
Everyone looked at William.

"He's not MY dog," William said.

"Well, that dog jumped in my window
and walked all over my hats," she said.

The woman shut the door with a bang.
William watched through the window.
The woman went back to her shop, and
Stanley lay down on the sidewalk
in front of the barber shop.

Three men came to get their hair cut,
but Stanley barked at them.

The barber looked at William. "Boy," he said,
"isn't that your dog?"

William looked at his shoes. "No," he said.
"He just followed me. He lives next door
to my house."

"Well," the barber said. "That dog is keeping
people out of my shop. There are people here
ahead of you, but I'll cut your hair now.
I don't want that dog around here.
Get up in the chair. Hurry."

William got up in the chair, and the barber
moved the chair around and started to work.

William's hair fell everywhere.

No one had ever cut William's hair
in such a hurry.

The barber moved the chair around again,
and William got down. He gave the money
to the barber and went outside
and got on his bicycle.

He rode home as fast as he could go,
and Stanley ran ahead of him.

Lucy was on the front steps.

"Dad's waiting for you inside," she said.

His father looked at William's hair.

"It looks fine," he said. "You weren't gone long. That's what a boy can do when he decides to hurry. We have a lot of time to get to the ball game."

"He's going some place, so that's why he hurried," Lucy said.

"It's the barber who hurried most of all," said William.

William and his father sat beside each other in the baseball park.

The wind was cool on the back of William's neck.

William and the Dog House

William Brown walked into the house
just as his mother picked up the telephone.

"Hello . . . . oh yes, Mrs. Bradley . . . .
Is that so ? . . . . Well, well . . . .
Yes, William will do that for you . . . .
Don't be worried about a thing."

William waited until she set the telephone down.

"What did Mrs. Bradley say ? Why did you say
'don't be worried' ? What do I have to do ?"

"The Bradleys are going away for a week or so,
and Mrs. Bradley wanted to know
if you will take care of their yard
and pick up the mail while they are away—"
William waited until she finished talking.
"—And," his mother said, "she wanted to know
if you will take care of the dog too."
"I would LIKE to take care of Stanley!"
William said. "And I'll take care of their yard
and everything too."

William hurried out of the house and ran across
his own yard and over to Mrs. Bradley's back door.

Mrs. Bradley showed him what to feed the dog,
and then she showed him how to water the grass.

"Don't be worried about a thing," William said.
"I'll take care of the yard and of Stanley too."

"I know you will," Mrs. Bradley said.

"I think I'll take Stanley's doghouse across the yard
to OUR house, while you're gone," said William.

Everyone waved good-by when Mr. and Mrs. Bradley went away in their car.

All the boys in the block helped William move the doghouse across the yard.

Stanley went with them.

"This dog knows a lot," William said. "He knows 'want-to-go-for-a-walk' and 'where's-the-cat.'"

At last the doghouse was set in William's yard by the back door.

William knew that everything would be fine.

41

When night came, Stanley sat on the grass
looking worried. William showed him
the doghouse.

"Don't be worried, Stanley," William said.
"It's the same old doghouse. Go on in."

Stanley backed away.

William decided that Stanley didn't know
what to do and that he would have
to show him. William crawled
into the doghouse.

Stanley crawled in too.

But now William couldn't get out.

He pushed at Stanley,
but Stanley thought William
was playing and Stanley
pushed back.

William was worried.

42

William wanted to get outside, but Stanley
was in his way. He called for help.

"DAD, help. Iucy. mom."

But no one answered.

It was getting hot in the doghouse,
and William was worried. He didn't know what to do.
He thought he would have to stay there all night.

Then he thought of something.

"Stanley," he said. "Where's the cat?
Where's the cat?"

Stanley got up at once and crawled outside
to look for the cat.

William crawled outside too.

"Come on, Stanley," William said.
"You can sleep on the floor by my bed tonight."
They went into the house. William showed Stanley
where to sleep. "There. Down on the floor,"
William said. "Down, Stanley!"

Stanley went to sleep on the floor
and didn't move until morning.

The next morning all the boys helped William
carry the doghouse across his own yard
and back to Mrs. Bradley's yard.

The Bradleys Come Home

It was Saturday, and William
was watering the Bradleys' grass.

"You have all the fun," Lucy said.
"You get to take care of Stanley,
and you get to water the grass too.
And I only get to watch. Let me water."

"All right," William said. "I'll let you.
But only if you keep the hose still. Only
if you don't flip water all over the place.
You have to do exactly as I say. Don't
flip the water around."

46

"All right," said Lucy.
"I'll do exactly as you say."

Lucy was standing with her back
against the oak tree. She took
the hose and held it still
for a long time.

Then she gave it one flip.

"You heard me tell you not to flip
the water around," William said.

"I heard," Lucy said.

"Then stop it. You got water
all over me," William said. "Stop it."

So Lucy held the hose very still.

47

William looked at Stanley, who was sleeping
under the oak tree.

Lucy took a long time to water
the grass. The grass looked nice and green.

Stanley woke up and walked over to William.
He pushed against William and then
wagged his tail. William gave him a pat,
and Stanley's tail wagged faster.

Mr. and Mrs. Bradley would be home any time now.

Mr. and Mrs. Bradley did not come home that day,
but next morning William heard Stanley barking.
He heard a car door shut with a bang. Then
he heard the other car door. He hurried outside.

Stanley jumped around and wagged his tail.

Mrs. Bradley took a little basket
into the house. Mr. Bradley took two
big boxes out of the back of the car.

Mrs. Bradley called to Mr. Bradley,
"Better call William right away!"

"William's here," Mr. Bradley called back.
"Hello there, William. Everything looks fine. Nice work,
William. We knew you would do a good job."

William was very pleased. "I liked doing it,"
he said.

"Mrs. Bradley and I have something for you,
William. It's a surprise. Your mother and father
said you could have it. We thought
you would be pleased. Come on in."

William and Stanley followed Mr. Bradley
into the house.

There in a basket was a little puppy.

"We knew you would like him," Mrs. Bradley said.
"Someday this puppy will look just like Stanley."

At first William didn't know what to say.
Then he knew.

"It's just exactly what I want," he said.

"We knew you would like him," Mrs. Bradley said.

"There's only one thing better than having
a dog next door," William said, "and that's having
a dog of your very own."

He picked up the puppy. It pushed against
William and licked his chin. And then it wagged
its tail, exactly as Stanley did.

50

Things I Like

I like a little ladybug
Crawling on my thumb,
I like a little humming-bird,
Hum-hum-hum-

I like a little sea shell,
And dandelion fuzz,
Or a brave little bumble-bee,
Buzz-buzz-buzz-

I like a little lizard
Hiding in the dark,
But most, I like a puppy,
Bark-bark-bark.

Patricia Miles Martin

52

Vowel Puzzles

Think of one vowel letter which can fit into all the blanks in one sentence. Then read the sentence.

1. Th_s sh_p w_ll take a tr_p.

2. The t_p is n_t in the b_x.

3. D_d c_n n_p on his b_ck.

4. A bird can s_ng and flap his w_ngs.

5. T_d m_t a p_t with a b_ll on his n_ck.

6. A d_ck having f_n in the s_n began

   to r_n.

7. A tr_tting horse named D_t st_pped on

   the t_p of a hill.

8. D_ck sl_d and h_t h_s sh_n.

9. A m_n s_t on t_n s_nd, then r_n

   b_ck to the l_nd.

10. Bad l_ck. We sat in the d_st and r_st

   on a st_mp.

ABOUT ANIMALS

How the Bear Got His Supper

There was no noise in the forest.

Rabbits hopped on soft little rabbit feet
in the wild grass, looking for their supper.
Chipmunks ran on soft little chipmunk feet
and ate their supper up in an old oak tree.
A little mouse came creeping . . . creeping . . .

There was no noise in the forest—
only the birds sang
in the top of the old tree.

56

And then, CRASH-BANG,
a bear—a big black bear—
came into the forest.
 The rabbits didn't move.
 The chipmunks were still.
 The mouse ran under a log.
 The birds called softly,
"Cheep . . . . cheep . . . ."

The bear stopped under the oak tree.

He was a hungry bear—a very hungry bear.

He looked up into the tree.

There in the oak tree was his supper—
a supper of fat acorns. But the acorns
were high—high up in the tree.

The hungry bear could not reach them.

But he knew how he would get his supper.

He climbed into the tree.

Up, up he climbed. But he did not reach
for the acorns.

He crawled out on a big branch of the tree.
He sat there and then he rocked the branch.
Up and down. Up and down.

And the branch broke with a CRASH-BANG.

Down they fell, branch and acorns
and big black bear. CRASH-BANG.

The bear rolled over. He sat up
and looked around. With his big, big paws,
he reached for the acorns.

He reached for more, and he ate his fill.

And while he ate his supper, the rabbits
and the chipmunks were still.
And only the birds called,
"Cheep . . . . cheep . . . ."

And when he was not hungry, the bear
went out of the forest with a crash and a bang.
CRASH-BANG.

And when he was gone, the rabbits looked
for their supper.

Chipmunks ran high up into the tree
and down again and hid acorns in the brush.

The little mouse came creeping . . . creeping . . .

Again there was no noise in the forest—
only the birds sang in the old oak tree.

Wild Things

On the side of a hill a little pack rat
is hunting for his supper. The pack rat
is hungry. And while he hunts, he is afraid—
very afraid—for the pack rat has many enemies.

And some of the pack rat's enemies are these:
Owl and Eagle, Fox and Bobcat, and

SNAKE.

Crawling—crawling, the snake is hunting
for his supper. He too is hungry.
And while he hunts, he is afraid, for the snake
has many enemies. And some of his enemies
are these: Owl and Eagle, Bobcat and

FOX.

63

The old fox barks at the moon. He is hungry.
He starts out to hunt for his supper.

He prowls over the hill and down again.

He prowls through the brush, and he is afraid.

When the fox was very little, he was afraid
of Owl and Eagle.

Now that he is old, he is afraid of

BOBCAT.

The bobcat prowls through the forest.

He prowls through the green forest
on his big, soft feet. He makes no noise.

He is very hungry and he is afraid.

He is afraid of

MAN.

Little Pronghorn

Alone, a little pronghorn lay waiting in the brush.
Far away, his mother ran across the open country.
A coyote was running after her. She led
the coyote far from the place where her
little pronghorn lay.

The coyote would not catch her for she
ran very fast—and no coyote could run
as fast as the mother pronghorn could run.

The little pronghorn lay very still.

Late that day Nan and her father
started for a ride. Nan saw the little pronghorn
in the brush. They stopped their horses.

"Where can its mother be?" Nan asked.

"I don't know," her father said, "but the
mother will not stay away long.
She will be back soon."

Then they heard the bark of a coyote
from far away. They heard the coyote bark again.

"The coyote is coming this way," Nan said.

"That coyote is prowling around looking for food.
He would like to find this little pronghorn here,"
her father said. "We'll have to take him with us."

He jumped from his horse and took
the little pronghorn and put him across Nan's lap.

The little pronghorn was only one day old,
and he was very small. He lay very still.

At home Nan gave him some milk. He was
very hungry.

Little Pronghorn was beautiful. He had
a red-brown coat. He had some white hair
on his face and around his tail
and on his stomach. His legs were very long.

"When he stands up, his legs look
like sticks," Nan said. "How can he ever learn
to run on those funny little stick legs!"

"It won't take him long to learn,"
her father said. "He will learn by the time
he's about three days old, and soon he will run
faster than the coyote. Pronghorns can run faster
than all other animals in the land."

On the open grassland when a pronghorn lies flat
against the ground, he looks like the ground
where he lies. Very soon he learns to lie flat
against the ground. If he lies very still without moving,
and if he lies very flat, his enemies will not see him.

But sometimes he is afraid.

Around the pronghorn's tail is a ring
of white hair. When a pronghorn is afraid,
the white hair on his tail stands up in the ring.
The ring of hair can be seen from far away,
flashing white in the light of the sun.

It tells other pronghorns to watch
for their enemies—to watch for coyote or eagle,
prowling bobcat or mountain lion.

When a pronghorn is about three days old,
it can run and play.

So, very soon, when Nan raced her horse
down the road, Little Pronghorn raced with her.
He seemed to fly.

The day came when it was time
for Little Pronghorn to go back to his herd.

"A pronghorn is wild," Nan said.
"He must go back to the others
and live with the herd."

One morning when she rode her horse,
and Little Pronghorn raced with her,
Nan saw a herd of pronghorns.

The herd was standing on a far hill.

The little pronghorn knew the herd was there.
His mother was with them.

He ran fast, away across the flat land
and up the hill. Nan watched him go.
He ran faster than he had ever run before.

Little Pronghorn did not look back.
On he went—on and on,
until he was safe with the herd
on the hill.

THE BEAVERS BUILD A HOUSE

The sun goes down and night will come soon.

Wild animals come softly from the woods.

They come to the pond to drink.

Two beavers swim across the pond.

It is time for them to go to work.

73

Beside the water are many young trees.
The beavers climb out of the water.
Each picks a young tree. And each stands
on its back legs and leans on its wide, flat tail.

They chew the bark of the young trees.
As they chew, chips fall to the ground.
The beavers chew almost through the trees.

A tree leans.

It leans a little more—

WHACK!

A beaver's tail hits the ground.

This is the beaver's way of saying DANGER.
One of the young trees is about to fall,
and the beavers hurry away from the falling tree.
They hurry to the pond and dive deep down
into the water away from danger.

The tree falls to the ground.
It falls with a great CRASH!

After a while the beavers come to the tree
where it lies on the ground. They chew off
the branches. Now they stop chewing and listen
for danger. They listen for the coyote
and the bobcat.

76

The beavers take the branches
from the young tree to make a house.
They carry the branches out into the water
and put them in the mud down deep in the pond.
    Again and again they carry branches.
In the pond they make a pile of branches
that is higher than the water. The pile
of branches can be seen above the water.
This is the floor of their house.

They work many nights building this house.

They carry armloads of mud—
then more and more armloads.

They put mud on the floor of branches.
They make a mud pile two feet high, on top
of the branches. Then they put sticks and
more mud on top of it all.

They dive deep under the water, and they dig
two tunnels. These two tunnels go through
the great pile of mud and branches
to the place where their house will be.

They start to dig a cave in the mud.
When they dig the cave, they carry
armloads of mud out through their tunnels.

At last they have a house to live in.
They leave one little hole in the top
of the house for air to come through.

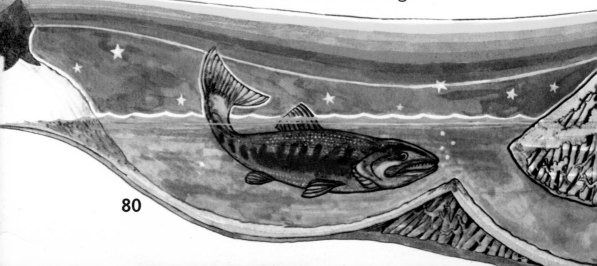

One side of the house is high,
and the other is low.

Their house is ready.

The beavers store food to last
all the winter long. Out through tunnels
they go for food. In through tunnels
they carry armloads of branches.

They take the branches to the low side
of the house.

Here on the low side they will eat.

They will sleep and rest on the high
side.

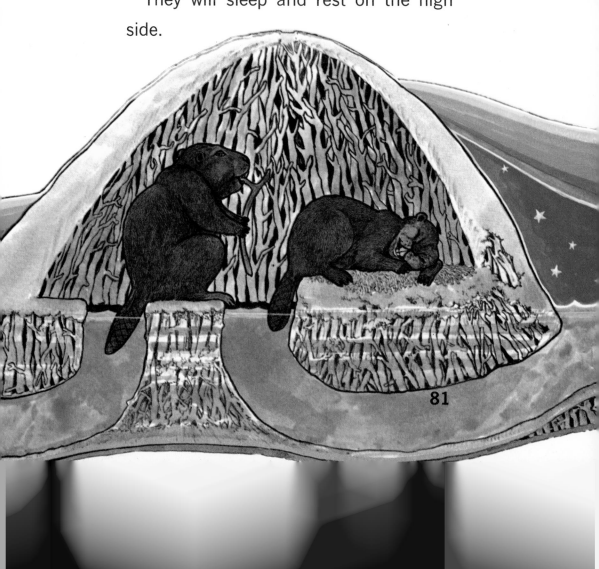

81

The nights are long, and snow falls.

Outside, far away, the bark of a hungry coyote is heard.

But in the beaver house two beavers are safe; safe from the coyote, safe from the bobcat, safe from all danger.

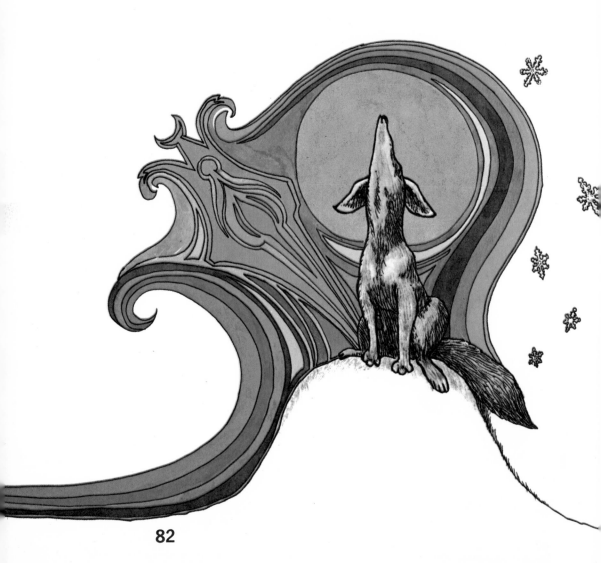

SYLVESTER JONES and THE VOICE IN THE FOREST

Sylvester Jones heard the voice
from the forest, and it was calling him.

"Syl-VES-ter. Syl-VES-ter."

It was as clear as his mother's voice
when she called him to supper.

There it was again—

"Syl-VES-ter. Syl-VES-ter."

83

Sylvester lived in a small house not far
from the forest with his mother and father.
They had two pigs and six chickens
and a small stand of corn. And that corn
was higher than Sylvester.

Every day Sylvester fed corn
to the pigs and the chickens.

One morning he sat on the steps, eating a slice of bread and jam.

When he had finished eating his bread and jam, Sylvester's feet took him into the house.

"The voice is calling again," Sylvester said to his mother. "Maybe it's a friend."

"I haven't heard a thing," she said. "Maybe you just think a voice is calling."

"I heard it," Sylvester said. "I heard it with my own ears. Can I go to the forest to find who's calling?"

"Well," his mother said. "If you heard it with your own ears, you may go when you have fed the pigs and the chickens."

Sylvester took a pail of corn. When the pigs and chickens were fed, his mother packed a lunch for him. She put his lunch in a pail. Sylvester picked up the pail.

Quietly he went into the forest.

Quietly he listened.
He heard a soft "Hoo-Hoo."
It was only a sleepy owl in a pine tree.

Quietly he waited.

He heard something in the brush.

But it was only a little brown rabbit
with long, long ears.

It flipped its long ears and hopped away.

Sylvester sat down on the ground and
he put his head on his arm.

"It can't be a boy. There isn't any boy
around here. It can't be a girl. There's
no girl around here." He listened.

"I'll wait and I'll watch," he said.

He listened so long and so quietly that
his ears hummed.

Then . . . . there it was!

Sylvester didn't move.

Under a pine tree was a fat valley quail.

And the valley quail nodded his head.

Sylvester waited.

The quail nodded his head again and said,

"Syl-VES-ter."

Sylvester reached into his lunch pail
and took out his lunch. There were two slices
of bread and jam. He put one slice on the ground.

The valley quail watched Sylvester.
Sylvester sat there without moving.

The quail came close.

When Sylvester picked up his lunch pail,
the quail called "Syl-VES-ter" and went flying off.

"I'll be back again," Sylvester said.

He hurried out of the forest and up the steps
to home.

At home he said to his mother,
"I know what the voice is. I know what
was calling me. It's a bird."

"You saw a valley quail," his mother said.
"I heard him too, while you were gone.
Listen. It's calling again.
That's the call of the valley quail.
'Syl-VES-ter. Syl-VES-ter.'"

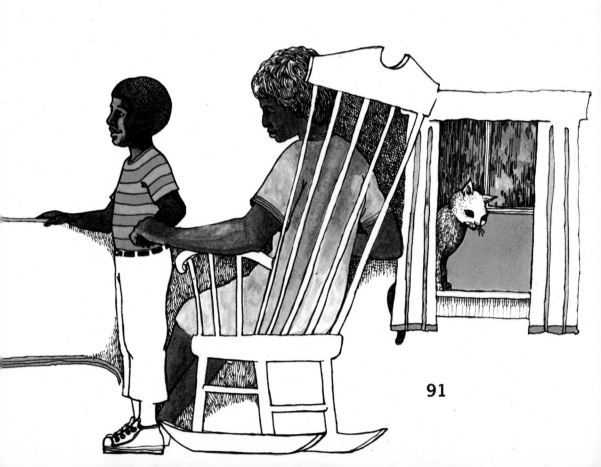

Now if someday you go out into the deep woods,
and if you see a valley quail, listen quietly. And if
you don't move, that quail will call Sylvester Jones.

Listen !

"Syl-VES-ter.

Syl-VES-ter."

If You Find a Little Feather

If you find a little feather,
a little white feather,
a soft and tickly feather,
            it's for you.

A feather is a letter
from a bird,
and it says,
"Think of me.
Do not forget me.
Remember me always.
Remember me forever.
Or remember me
at least
until
the little feather
is
lost."

So . . .
. . . if you find a little feather,
a little white feather,
a soft and tickly feather,
        it's for you.
        Pick it up
            and . . .
                put it in your pocket!

Beatrice Schenk de Regniers

93

Animal Babies

Have you ever seen a baby animal just after it was born? Read about three kinds of newly born animal babies.

Black bear mothers have from one to four babies at a time. The babies are very small. New baby bears cannot see. They have no fur.

Baby chipmunks are born without fur. Their eyes are closed at first. There may be four or five in a family.

New baby rabbits have no fur and they are blind for a while. There may be from four to seven in a litter.

Ask your teacher to make a chart like the one on the next page. Then fill in the chart from the facts that you have just read.

	bears	chipmunks	rabbits
How many babies are born?			
Can the babies see when they are born?			
Are the babies covered with fur?			

Look at your chart when you have filled it in. Can you sum up what you see? From the facts on the chart, which of the sentences below could you say were true?

Rabbit, chipmunk and bear babies:

1. are born blind.
2. can run around right away after they are born.
3. are quite helpless at first.
4. have no fur at first.
5. play with each other right away.
6. are the only animal babies born without fur.
7. have brothers and sisters born at the same time.

Things to Think About

Look at the picture. Then decide which of these things you might hear or see in the pond.

water splashing	a chipmunk chattering
a rabbit munching grass	a beaver's house
a frog croaking	meat frying

Look at the picture. Which of these could you see or hear in the forest?

a bear growling	a flash of color
a brown leaf	a branch snapping
high heels clicking	branches of trees
a bobcat howling	a beaver swimming

STORIES
EVERYONE
WILL LIKE

The Raccoon and Mrs. McGinnis

A little raccoon who was almost tame
lived in an old apple tree. He had a black mask
on his face and six black rings on his tail.
   There, in the woods by the old apple tree,
was a little house, where Mrs. McGinnis lived.

Mrs. McGinnis had one cow and two pigs.
She took armloads of hay to the cow
and pails of corn to the pigs.

And every night the cow and the pigs
went to sleep under the apple tree.

Then she put a slice of bread on the doorstep
for the raccoon, and the raccoon knew
that the bread was for him.

One night she was standing
in front of her house, as she often did.
She looked up and saw a star.

"That's the first star I have seen tonight,
indeed it is," she said. "I will make a wish.
Indeed I will." She looked up at the star.
"I wish for a little barn, so my cow and my pigs
will be safe from the wind and the rain."
Then she put a slice of bread on her step.

99

After Mrs. McGinnis had gone to bed,
the raccoon came down from the tree
and picked up the bread.

He walked into the woods until he came
to a river. Beside the river he swished
the bread in the water, because
that is what a raccoon often does.
When the bread was wet, he ate it.

Because he was still hungry, he started to look
for something more to eat. Just as he started
to look, he heard something coming down the road.
Two men came along on their horses. The raccoon
hid in back of a tree.

100

The men got down from their horses.

"Mrs. McGinnis is not far from here," the first man said. "We will leave our horses here, and we will go to Mrs. McGinnis's house. We will go very quietly, and we will take her cow and pigs. She will not know they are gone until morning."

The men put black masks over their faces
and started down the road. The raccoon followed.
The men made no noise. When they reached
the apple tree, they took the cow and the pigs
and started back through the woods.
The little raccoon still followed.

He followed quietly. Then he stepped on
a small branch, and the branch broke with a CRACK.

"What was that?" asked the first man.

"It was nothing," said the other.

"Little night animals often play here."

102

Then a small rock rolled down the hill
and into the river. It made a splash.

"What was that?" asked the first man.

"It was nothing," said the other. "Nothing at all.
Often little fish jump and splash in the water."

Everything was very still until a rabbit
ran down the road.

"I think someone is following us,"
the first man said.

The little raccoon thought he would climb
a tree because there he would be safe from danger.
He climbed up and looked around the tree
to see where the men were.

In the moonlight only the black mask
of the little raccoon could be seen.

THE MEN WERE LOOKING RIGHT AT HIM.

"It is another masked bandit,"
said the first man.

"Don't shoot." said the other.
"You may take our cow and our pigs."
"Take our money too," said the first man.
"ONLY PLEASE DON'T SHOOT."

And as he ran to his horse,
he tossed a fat moneybag to the ground.
The men went off down the road
as fast as their horses could go.

The raccoon climbed down and
picked up the moneybag. He took it to the river
and swished it in the water.

The cow and the pigs started down the road
that led to the little house,
and the raccoon followed with the moneybag.

Because he often looked on the step for bread,
he went there to look. There was nothing on the step,
so he dropped the moneybag and went up the tree
to his bed.

In the morning Mrs. McGinnis came outside.

"What is this? It is a moneybag! Indeed it is!
My wish has come true! Indeed it has!
NOW I can have a barn for my cow and my pigs."

Some men came, and soon there was a barn
where no barn had been before.

106

At night Mrs. McGinnis would often lean against the apple tree, look up at the stars, and say, "My cow and my pigs are safe in the barn, and ALL because I wished upon a star." That is what she thought !

Then she would put something on her step.

And after a while the little raccoon, who was almost tame, would climb down from the tree. Then he would look on the step because he knew that she had put a slice of bread there, just for him.

Johnny Appleseed

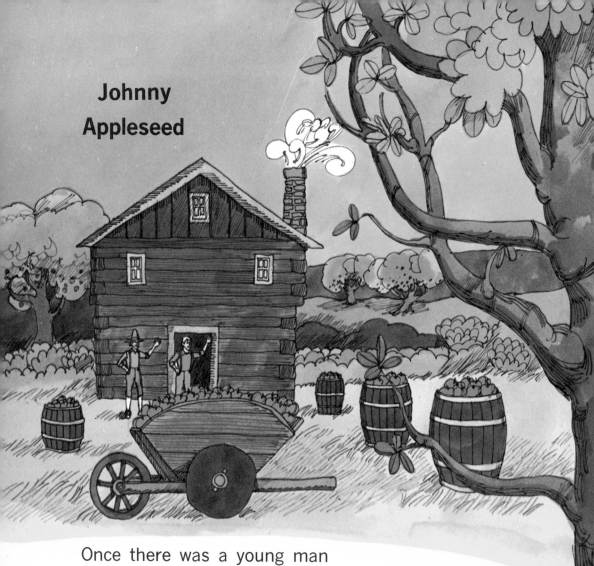

Once there was a young man
named Johnny Appleseed, who watched men working
in a cider mill. Cider was being made from apples.
When the cider was made, the men
threw all the apple seeds away.

Young Johnny decided that he would pick up
the seeds that the men threw away.

108

One day he took the many seeds
that he had picked up and put them in a big sack.

Johnny knew there were no apple trees
in the West.

"The people out there in the West
would like to have apple trees," thought Johnny.

He decided that he would go west
to plant the apple seeds.

With a sack on his back and
a tin pan on his head, Johnny started west.
He wore the tin pan for a hat. He wore
it every day, but when the time came to eat,
he made his supper in it.

When he came to a river, he stopped.

"Seeds like ground near a river,"
he thought. "I will plant apple seeds
in the ground near the water."

And he planted seeds.

Often he saw mountain lions
prowling through the forest.

On he went, down through the green valleys
and up over the hills.

When he came to a farm in the valley,
he threw his sack from his back and
started to work.

He planted seeds for the farmer.

"Water the seeds well," Johnny said
to the farmer. "Make a small fort
out of the branches of the pine tree.
Set a small fort around each seed
until a young green shoot comes
through the ground. Leave the fort standing.
If you leave the fort standing
until the little tree is as high as a boy,
one day you will have big apple trees."

"It will be a fine thing to have apple trees
on this farm," the farmer said.

"One day you will have big trees
to shade those who stop to rest
under the green branches. In the springtime
pink and white blossoms will make your trees
beautiful," Johnny said. "And in the fall
you will have red apples to eat."

Then Johnny went on his way.

"There goes Johnny Appleseed,"
the farmer said. "He planted seeds
that other men threw away."

And the farmer set a little fort
of pine branches around the place
where each seed was planted,
and he watered the ground well.

When Johnny planted all the seeds
that were in his sack, he went back
to the cider mill to get more seeds.

Again he went west.

Many times he went back and
forth—back and forth—from
cider mill to farms, from farms
to cider mill.

Johnny didn't care what he wore.
Often he wore a coat that was too big
and pants that were too small. He
sometimes wore one boot and one shoe.
At other times he wore no boots or shoes.

Sometimes he rode a horse.

More often he walked, carrying his sack
against his back.

When he walked, he heard the call
of the coyote and saw snakes crawling
over the ground near the river.

After a while all the farmers in the West
knew Johnny Appleseed, who followed his own path
back and forth—back and forth.

"Here comes Johnny Appleseed," the farmer said.
"He plants seeds near the river and on the farms.
He plants the seeds that other men threw away."

Everywhere, Johnny found friends.

On the farms, the farmers were his friends.

In the forest, the Indians were his friends.

And he was not afraid of mountain lions or bears,
wild hogs or snakes.

And in the West there were apple trees
where there had been no apple trees before,
because strange young Johnny planted the seeds.

114

The Purple Cow

Gelett Burgess

I never saw a Purple Cow,
  I never hope to see one;
But I can tell you, anyhow,
  I'd rather see than be one!

115

Crispin's Crispian

Once upon a time there was a funny dog named Crispin's Crispian. He was named Crispin's Crispian because—
he belonged to himself.

116

In the mornings he woke himself up
and gave himself some bread and milk
for his breakfast.

Then after breakfast he took himself
for a walk. And he went wherever he wanted to go.

He walked until he came to the country,
where there were lots of cats and rabbits.

The cats and rabbits jumped and ran.
So Crispian jumped and ran after them.

He didn't catch them because
he ran bang into a little boy.

"Who are you and who do you belong to?"
asked the little boy.

"I am Crispin's Crispian and
I belong to myself," said Crispian.
"Who and what are you?"

"I am a boy," said the boy,
"and I belong to myself."

"I am so happy," said Crispin's Crispian.
"Come and live with me."

So the boy walked on with Crispian
and threw him sticks to chase
all through the morning.

"I'm hungry," said Crispin's Crispian.

"I'm hungry too," said the boy's little boy.

So they went to the shop—

"To get his poor dog a bone," Crispian said.

"To get a lamb chop and some vegetables,
a green- vegetable and a yellow vegetable,"
the little boy said.

Now because Crispin's Crispian
belonged to himself, he gave himself
the bone and trotted home.

And the boy took the lamb chop
and the vegetables and trotted home
with Crispin's Crispian.

Crispin's Crispian lived in a doghouse
in a garden.

And there was a place for the boy
to live there with him.

And there Crispian had a little bedroom
where he hid his bones.

And he had windows to look out of
and a garden to run around in
any time he wanted to run around in it.

And he had a little room where he fixed himself
a good dinner three times a day, because
he liked to eat. He liked beef and soup.

Late that day he made a dinner of bone soup
with beef in it. He gave some of this soup
to the boy, and the boy liked it. The boy
put some of his green and yellow vegetables
into the soup.

And what did Crispian do with his dinner?
Did he put it in his stomach?
Yes, indeed.
He put it into his fat little stomach.

And what did the boy do with his dinner?
Did he put it in his stomach?
Yes, indeed.
He put it into his fat little stomach.

121

Crispin's Crispian liked everything
at the right time—
dinner at dinnertime,
lunch at lunchtime,
breakfast in time for breakfast,
and sunrise at sunrise,
and sunset at sunset.

And at bedtime—
At bedtime he liked everything
in its own place—
the stars and the moon in the sky,
and himself in his own little bed.
And then what did he do?

122

Then he curled in a warm little heap.
He curled in that warm little heap and
went to sleep. And he dreamed his own dreams.

That was what the dog who belonged
to himself did.

And what did the boy who belonged
to himself do ?

The boy who belonged to himself
curled in a warm little heap. He curled
in that warm little heap and went to sleep.
And he dreamed his own dreams.

That was what the boy who belonged
to himself did.

Puddlejumper

Puddlejumper was a little trolley car.
He was a good little trolley. But he was old
and his paint was cracked and his wheels squeaked.
Once the little trolley car had been new,
with flashing red paint, and not a squeak
in his wheels.

124

For many years Puddlejumper and
Mr. Mopsey, the man who ran the trolley car,
took the fathers of the city of Pineville
to and from work.

They took the mothers of Pineville shopping.
And they took the boys and girls of Pineville
to school.

Puddlejumper had liked that. He liked
the laughing, happy people.

Each night Mr. Mopsey had put Puddlejumper
in the carbarn. He had patted his headlight and said,
"Happy day." Then he had gone home.

And each night Puddlejumper had answered softly,
"Happy day," but Mr. Mopsey had not heard him.

Happy days they had been, every one.

But now Puddlejumper was not happy.

He was waiting for Mr. Mopsey,
and while he waited, tears, and still more tears,
fell down like rain.

"Stop sniffling, stop sniffling,"
said the big new bus that was standing near.
"What if this IS your last day on the streets
of Pineville, and what if you ARE going
to be sold for junk? Who cares if you're sold?
Stop your sniffling and let me sleep."

Puddlejumper stopped sniffling.

"It's all right for you to talk that way,"
said Puddlejumper, "because you're going to take
my place. I don't want to be sold for junk.
My paint is cracked and my wheels squeak,
but I'm still a good trolley car."

"That's right," said the bus. "Everyone knows
you will last a long, long time. But you're out of date.
You make too much noise with your rattle and squeak.
And you're not fast! You're just out of date, that's all.
No more sniffling now. Zzzzzzzzzz."
The big bus fell asleep.

"To be sold for junk!" thought Puddlejumper.
"I won't ever see Mr. Mopsey again! Oh no, no, no!"
Tears splashed down upon his tracks.

Mr. Mopsey didn't look sad the next morning.
Puddlejumper heard him whistle as he came
into the barn.

"How can he feel so happy?" thought Puddlejumper.
"This is our last day with each other."

Mr. Mopsey sat down. "Well, Puddlejumper,"
he said. "We have a little time before we must start.
And I am going to tell you a secret.
A little secret just for you and me.
This is my last trip over the streets of Pineville.
They wanted me to run that big bus over there,
but I said no. I have always wanted to work for myself.
I don't want to run a trolley. I'm going to work
for myself."

The door of the carbarn opened, and a man waved them to go ahead.

Rattle, rattle, rattle! Squeak, squeak, squeak! Puddlejumper and Mr. Mopsey went out of the carbarn for their last trip over the streets of Pineville.

Puddlejumper and Mr. Mopsey reached the end of their line. They stopped for a little while as they always had.

Before them was a wide street. Trucks and buses and cars whizzed back and forth.

"Just the place," said Mr. Mopsey. "Just the place."

And he walked to the other end of Puddlejumper, and they started back.

Puddlejumper thought about Mr. Mopsey's secret
all the way to the carbarn. Mr. Mopsey
was going to work for himself, and Puddlejumper
was going to the junk yard !

The little trolley car was sad indeed.
But Mr. Mopsey wasn't sad. He stopped Puddlejumper,
patted his headlight and said, "Happy day,
Puddlejumper." He whistled as he walked away.

Happy day, indeed !

For a week Puddlejumper sat in the carbarn.
And whenever he heard the sound of voices,
he began to shake all over.

When, oh when, was he going to be sold for junk ?

131

Then one day he heard a voice say,
"This is the old trolley car."

Some men put tracks up to the back
of the big truck. They rolled Puddlejumper up on it
and took him away.

"This is the end," thought Puddlejumper.
"This is it." Tears splashed down like raindrops.

Then the truck stopped. The men started to roll
him down, and Puddlejumper looked around.

"This isn't a junk yard," he thought.
"This is the end of the line."

Then there was Mr. Mopsey.

"Put him down here, boys," Mr. Mopsey said.
"Don't drop him now."

And they set Puddlejumper down, right near
the end of the line.

Mr. Mopsey went to work and washed
Puddlejumper. He washed outside and inside.
Outside he painted Puddlejumper's roof red
and his sides green, with a little bit of yellow
for trim.

Inside Mr. Mopsey put in a long counter
and nine little chairs. At one end of the counter
he put in a kitchen—a very small kitchen.

Soon from Puddlejumper's kitchen there were good smells of doughnuts and coffee coming out into the wide street.

Trucks stopped. Cars stopped. Buses stopped. People got out of them. They went up to Puddlejumper and looked at the sign just above the headlight.

The sign said:

"TROLLEY CAR INN."

"So this is Mr. Mopsey's secret," Puddlejumper thought. "This is his secret—doughnuts and coffee!"

Puddlejumper is happy now. No tears ever splash down like raindrops. All day happy, laughing people are sitting along the counter, having doughnuts and coffee. And at the end of the counter in his little kitchen, Mr. Mopsey whistles as he makes doughnuts and more doughnuts, and coffee and more coffee.

Every night Mr. Mopsey washes his little kitchen, and he washes off the counter. Then he pats Puddlejumper's headlight, and says, "Happy day."

"Happy day," Puddlejumper answers softly.

Far away the lights of the city of Pineville wink at a very happy Puddlejumper, as he goes to sleep under the stars.

Wish Riddles

Can you guess what we are wishing for before you come to the end of the riddle? STOP when you come to [?] See if you have guessed. STOP again at the next [?] and guess. How soon can you guess?

I need one for the party. [?] Mother could buy one. [?] I found an old one but it won't fit. [?] I tried to make one but it didn't fit. [?] I have a long dress and a pink fur hat and I need this to go with it. [?] It needs two holes in it. [?] I will put it on my face. [?] Then the others won't know who I am. [?] What is it?

Not many people own one of these. [?] Some wild animals would like one. [?] A boy would too. [?] Raccoons are fond of what I'm wishing for. [?] You could hide in one in the summer. [?] I want one so that I can climb it. [?] It takes a long time for one to grow. [?] It grows from an acorn. [?] Have you guessed?

Which?

Look at the pictures. Can you answer the questions below?

Which one or ones

could become a farmer?

is a learner?

is a climber?

might become a batter?

could be a swimmer?

will be a runner?

will grow taller?

is bigger than the others?

will never be smaller?

grows higher each year?

is greener in summer?

will not grow younger?

Make up questions of your own, using words that end in *er*.

Make-Believe

The words in each box tell about something in that box that is make-believe. Draw pictures of the make-believe things. Show your pictures to others. Let them decide what they are.

a pink cob that can thump on a stump	a cork that can work a torch
a plank sunk in a pink pond	a snake that can shake a rake
a toad that can bow low	a lamb on a limb with a thumb

Make your own make-believe words by putting one or two letters in the blanks. Then draw pictures to show what the words tell.

1. a big __ell

2. a funny __ilk

3. a sad __ank

4. a pretty __ill

5. some happy __eeps

6. a silly __isk

138

ONE WAY

BUS STOP

NO PARKING

139

4
THE
CITY

Song of the Train

Clickety-clack,
Wheels on the track,
This is the way
They begin the attack:
Click-ety-clack,
Click-ety-clack,
Click-ety, *clack*-ety,
Click-ety
Clack.

140

Clickety-clack,
Over the crack,
Faster and faster
The song of the track:
Clickety-clack,
Clickety-clack,
Clickety, clackety,
Clackety
Clack.

Riding in front,
Riding in back,
Everyone hears
The song of the track:
Clickety-clack,
Clickety-clack,
Clickety, *clickety,*
Clackety
Clack.

David McCord

141

Neighborhood Parade

All the boys and girls in Fred Hill's block were talking about pet parades.

"We could have a pet parade of our own," Fred said.

"It could be a neighborhood parade," said Henry. "We could take our pets."

"I have a puppy," Jane Ann said.

"I have a fish," said Henry.

They went home to tell their mothers and fathers about it.

"All the boys and girls in the neighborhood are going to take their pets and parade around the outside of the park," Fred said to his mother. "We will start right here at our front door."

"I will go along," said his mother.

"I want to go," said Fred's little sister, Amy. Amy wore a fur cap with a long tail.

"Mom," Fred said. "It's summer. If you take Amy to the parade, make her take off that fur cap. It's too hot for fur."

"It's not too hot for me," said Amy. "I LIKE it."

"And she can't walk in the parade," Fred said. "She's too little."

"Your sister and I will follow you along the sidewalk," his mother said.

Then Fred thought of something. "Mom," he said. "I don't have a pet." ·

"Maybe Mrs. Gray will let you borrow her cat," his mother said.

Saturday morning was a good morning for the parade. There wasn't a cloud in the sky. Right after breakfast Fred hurried to see Mrs. Gray.

"Mrs. Gray," he said. "We're going to have a parade today. We're going to take our pets. Can I borrow your cat for a little while ?"

"I'm sorry, Fred," Mrs. Gray said. "You are too late. Billy took the cat."

He asked all along the block.

"I'm sorry, Fred," Mr. Black said. "Dan took our dog."

Everyone was sorry, but Fred was sorry most of all.

Then he rang Mrs. Green's bell.

"Mrs. Green," he said. "I know you don't want dogs in your apartment house, but I'd like to live here. My dog would like it too. He knows this neighborhood."

"No," Mrs. Green said, "I don't want dogs in my apartment house."

"He is a GOOD dog," William said. "He doesn't bark much. He picks up all the litter he finds in the street. Your yard would always be clean. Chips would pick up every bit of torn paper—every bit of litter.

"He picks up things that are lost too. When he finds something, he comes carrying it to me, and I take it back where it belongs. We could be your Lost and Found Department."

Mrs. Green smiled. "So far, William, we get along very well without a Lost and Found Department."

William was not happy. He started home to his old brownstone house.

Chips trotted off by himself. After a while he came back with a toy bear. He gave the toy bear to William. William took it back to Jill Gray, and came home and sat on the steps of his old brownstone house.

When Chips came home again, he walked proudly, carrying a handbag. He gave it to William.

"Thank you," William said. He hurried inside his house. "Look what Chips found," he said to his mother. "It has money in it. It rattles!"

"Open it and see if there is a name inside," she said.

William opened the handbag.

"There is a lot of money here," he said. He looked and found a paper with a name on it. "It's Mrs. Green's!" he said.

William and Chips ran all the way to the apartment house.

Mrs. Green was standing on the front walk, talking to Mrs. Barber. "I don't know WHERE I could have left it," she said. "I was on my way downtown with the rent money, when I saw that my handbag was gone."

"Here it is!" William called.

"William," Mrs. Green said. "WHERE did you find it?"

"I didn't find it," William said. "My DOG found it!"

"Well," Mrs. Green said. "Well." She opened the handbag. "Everything is here." She looked at Mrs. Barber. "Mrs. Barber, I don't think the people in our apartment house would mind having ONE dog living here, do you ?"

"I'd like to have a dog like Chips," Mrs. Barber said.

"William," Mrs. Green said. "Go home and tell your mother that I'd like to have your family here." She shut her handbag with a click. She patted Chips. "It will be a very good thing to have a dog here. I think that every apartment house needs a good Lost and Found Department," she said.

Red Tulips

Henry lived on the first floor of a big apartment house.

In front of the apartment house was a small garden.

In this garden Henry's father had planted red tulip bulbs.

The tulip bulbs bloomed in the springtime.

Each springtime there were more and more tulips.

One fall when the tulips had stopped blooming, and their leaves were brown, Henry's father said, "The tulip bulbs have multiplied. There are too many of them. We will take some of them out."

So Henry and his father dug up the tulip bed and raked it fine with a rake.

When they had planted the bulbs, many of them were left over.

"Now what shall we do with the tulip bulbs?" Henry's father said.

"I would like to ask my friends if they want them," Henry said.

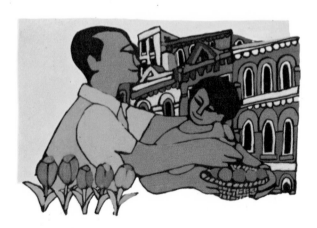

"Good," said his father. "Ask your friends."

Henry put the bulbs in a big basket.

He looked up at his apartment building.

On the second floor there were many window boxes.

Henry went up the steps and knocked at every door.

Everyone on the second floor was glad to have tulip bulbs for their window boxes.

On the next floor he knocked on Mrs. Black's door.

"Would you like to have some tulip bulbs?" Henry asked.

And Mrs. Black, who had no window box, said, "I'd be glad to have some tulip bulbs. Tulips always tell me that spring has come. I'll put them in pots and set them on my window sill."

159

When Henry got to the very top floor, he had only one tulip bulb left. On this top floor, little Mrs. May lived alone.

"Would you like a tulip bulb?" Henry asked. "I'm sorry I have only one left."

"I don't have a thing to plant it in," Mrs. May said. "But I'm glad to have one bulb. I will FIND something to plant it in."

So all the people in the apartment house planted tulips that day.

Winter passed and then spring came.

With water and with sun, the bulbs grew in the little garden outside the apartment house.

160

With water and with sun, they grew in window boxes. They grew in brown pots.

First there were wide leaves, and then came the tulips.

In all the windows in that apartment house red tulips bloomed.

They bloomed in window boxes and in brown pots.

And on the very top floor in Mrs. May's apartment, one beautiful red tulip bloomed in a blue teapot.

The people who went past the apartment house saw the red tulips blooming there.

They could all see that Henry was everyone's friend.

Washington Monument

Jefferson Memorial

162

Lincoln Memorial

The United States Capitol Building and the Surrounding Area

A Great City

When our country was young, the city of Washington, D.C. was built. The city called Washington, D.C. was built in a forest.

It was built near two beautiful rivers.

Wild geese winged their way across the sky, and frogs called from the rivers.

164

Trees were cut down and the great capitol building was built. Our laws were made in the capitol building.

A house was built. The President of the United States would live in this house.

At that time there was a park near the President's house. And people let their horses and cows, sheep and pigs graze in the park.

Today in that same park there are no horses or cows, sheep or pigs. It is a beautiful park for all people to see.

166

There are many things to see in the city— ponds, dogwood trees, and cherry trees.

This is a city of many monuments.

The highest of all is the George Washington Monument. This monument helps all of us remember George Washington, the first President of the United States.

Inside this monument is an elevator.

Boys and girls from all over the country ride in the elevator to the top.

Inside the monument are many steps. If boys and girls do not want to ride in the elevator, they may climb these steps that wind up and up.

When they reach the top, they see the United States Capitol building with its white dome.

They see many monuments.

They see far off over the winding rivers. They see Arlington Cemetery where lie those who died for our country.

The boys and girls look over this beautiful city—this great city, Washington, D.C.—the capital of our country.

Boys in an Apartment House

Mrs. O'Leary lived alone
In a little apartment all her own.
She liked the people down the hall,
And those upstairs. But most of all
She liked the boys.
"But they DO make noise,"
Said Mrs. O'Leary.

In the upstairs apartment over her head,

Two noisy boys got ready for bed.

They laughed and sang and banged the door.

They threw their shoes upon the floor.

Mrs. O'Leary counted to four.

"Good," she said.

"The boys are in bed.

They are very nice boys,

But I don't like noise."

Said Mrs. O'Leary.

170

She thought and thought. "This isn't right.
It is MUCH too noisy, day and night!"
So she moved upstairs to the very top.
She could almost hear a feather drop,
Except when jets went flashing by.
She sat by her window and looked at the sky.
"I miss those boys
And their happy noise,"
Said Mrs. O'Leary.
"There is no one around to bang a door,
Or throw a shoe upon the floor."

171

She decided she would move away.
She packed her things that very day.
And move she did. Where did she go?
To her old apartment down below!
And noisy boys above her head,
Jumped about getting ready for bed,
And laughed and sang and banged the door,
And threw their shoes upon the floor.

"If you like boys,"
Said Mrs. O'Leary,
"You have to like noise,"
Said Mrs. O'Leary.

172

The Clover Street Trio

Jen and Linda and Kate lived on Clover Street. They were always together. Because they were three, everyone called them the Clover Street Trio.

They always walked to school together, and they came home together.

Then Jen would hurry out of her flat. Linda and Kate would hurry out of their apartment houses.

Some days one of the girls had three apples. Some days one would have three doughnuts. They were best friends and they liked Clover Street.

173

Some days they hunted in the clover that grew along the street.

"My grandmother says that if you find a four-leaf clover, you will have good luck," Jen said.

"We don't need a four-leaf clover," Kate said, "because we have good luck now. We live on Clover Street."

"If we want to skate, our sidewalk is just right," Jen said.

"And we always want to skate," said Linda.

"It's good for jump-rope too," Kate said. Two held the rope and one jumped.

174

One morning there was a new girl in school.

Miss Donna said, "This is Trudy. I hope everyone will be kind to Trudy."

"I'll show her where to put her coat," Johnny said.

"I'll show her where we keep our lunches," said Bob.

175

After school the Clover Street Trio sat on Jen's front steps, and they had a surprise.

The door of the apartment house across the street opened, and out came Trudy.

"Look," said Jen. "It's the new girl, Trudy."

"I guess she moved into the apartment," Kate said. "Do we want to ask her to play?"

No one answered.

"We can think about it after a while," Linda said.

"Let's skate," said Jen.

The Clover Street Trio skated up and down the block. They did not look at Trudy.

Trudy watched.

Jen and Linda and Kate jumped rope until Trudy went into her apartment house.

After Trudy went inside her apartment house, the Clover Street Trio sat on Linda's steps.

Linda sat with her chin in her hands. "I wonder how it would be if you and Trudy were the Clover Street Trio. I wonder how it would be if I watched," she said.

"I wonder," said Kate.

"Would we have more fun if we asked Trudy to play?" Jen asked.

"Maybe four would be better than three," Kate said.

The next morning Kate and Jen and Linda were waiting when Trudy and her mother came down their steps.

"Trudy can walk with us," Jen said.

"We will take her to school," said Kate.

"Thank you!" Trudy's mother said. She waved good-by to Trudy.

The four girls walked to school together.

"Do you have skates?" Linda asked.

Trudy nodded.

"Do you like to jump rope?" Jen asked.

Trudy nodded again.

"What do you have in your lunch bag?" Kate asked.

"Cake for one thing," Trudy said.

"Trade you for an apple," said Jen.

178

When they reached the schoolyard, they all went inside together.

"Here comes the Clover Street Trio," Bob said.

"There can't be a trio with four people," said Johnny.

"We have a new name now," Kate said. "WE'RE the Four-Leaf Clovers."

AT THE BUS STATION

Charlie was getting ready to go to the bus station to meet his friend, Ken, who was coming to stay all night.

Charlie's little sister, Billy May, wanted to whistle through her teeth, but she couldn't. One tooth was loose. The loose tooth moved back and forth.

"I want to go to the bus station too," Billy May said.

"I don't want to take her because she always loses something. Then we have to hunt for what she has lost," Charlie said.

"If she leaves her hat at home, she can't lose her hat," said their mother. "And if she keeps her coat on, she can't lose a thing. Why don't you take her?"

181

So now Billy May and Charlie were in the bus station waiting for Ken's bus.

All the other people in the station were waiting for buses too. Some were reading  newspapers. Some were eating out of paper bags.

Other people were walking around. They were laughing and calling to each other.

A great voice boomed out, telling about buses that were coming and buses that were going, but no one seemed to listen.

A girl was putting  money in a
popcorn machine. Pigeons were flying
around her, waiting for popcorn to drop
to the floor.

Billy May walked over to see the pigeons.
There were machines for everything.

A very little boy couldn't reach the gum
machine and a big boy helped him.

At another machine a man was
getting coffee in a paper cup. 183

There were more machines
in one place than Billy May
had ever seen before.

Buses came and went. Air brakes
puffed and doors banged open.
People stepped down
from buses and
other people climbed on.
At last
a bus came, and
when the door
opened, Charlie's
friend, Ken, was the
first one off.

POPCORN

"Come on, let's go home," Charlie said.
He looked for Billy May.

She was near the popcorn stand,
sitting on her heels.

Pigeons were flying low
near her head.

Pigeons were on the floor around
her feet. Pigeons were everywhere.

"What are you doing?" Charlie asked.
"What did you lose?"

"I lost my loose tooth. I'm looking
for it," Billy May said.

185

At home, their mother opened the door.

"Hello, Ken," she said. "I am glad to see you. Come in, Charlie." She looked at Billy May. "I see you didn't lose your coat."

"But she lost something," Charlie said. "She lost her tooth."

"A loose tooth is a good thing to lose," Billy May said proudly. And she whistled through the place where the tooth had been.

Mrs. Peck–Pigeon

Mrs. Peck-Pigeon
Is picking for bread,
Bob-bob-bob
Goes her little round head.
Tame as a pussy-cat
In the street,
Step-step-step
Go her little red feet.
With her little red feet
And her little round head,
Mrs. Peck-Pigeon
Goes picking for bread.

Eleanor Farjeon

187

Change a Letter

Take *a* away from *ax*. Put a letter in its place and have a word for a big animal once used on farms.

Take *i* out of *fist*. Put a letter in its place and have a word that tells how you move when you are in a hurry.

Take *a* from *ball*. Put another letter in its place and have a word that stands for something that rings.

Take *x* from *next*. Put a letter in its place and have a word for the home of a crow.

Change the *a* in *crab* so that you will have a word meaning a bed for a baby.

Change the first letter of *found* so that you will have a word which tells the shape of most balls.

Put two letters in place of the *st* in *stick* and have a word for what some buildings are made of.

188

One Will Do

Read the two sentences in each set. Then think of one word which fits both meanings.

1. If you ride in an airplane you do this.

This is an insect which people do not like.

2. Most people do this to raw meat.

If a man is one, he sometimes wears a tall white hat.

3. When you do this, you lie down and turn over and over.

This is the name of something you can eat for dinner.

One word will do for two of the pictures. Can you find the pictures that match?

1.  2. 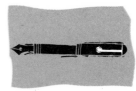 3.

4. 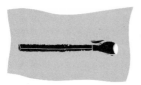 5.  6.

What Is in the Block?

Read all the words around the block. Then read the sentence in the block. Think of a word that is like the other words and fits the sentence. What is it?

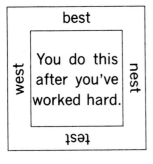

best

west — You do this after you've worked hard. — nest

test

lack

sack — Your foot makes one in the snow. — pack

crack

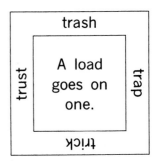

trash

trust — A load goes on one. — trap

trick

flake

flock — It comes from a fire. — flit

flash

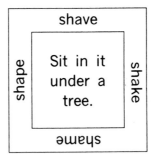

shave

shape — Sit in it under a tree. — shake

shame

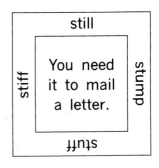

still

stiff — You need it to mail a letter. — stump

stuff

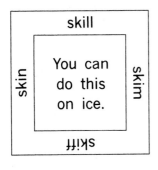

skill

skin — You can do this on ice. — skim

skiff

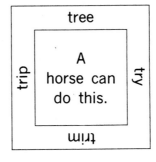

tree

trip — A horse can do this. — try

trim

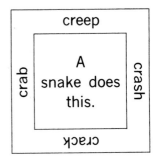

creep

crab — A snake does this. — crash

crack

190

WHAT WOULD YOU DO?

5

DOWN THE MISSISSIPPI

Augustus was asleep in the houseboat where he lived with his sister Gloriana, his little brother Jupiter, Pop, Mom, Tom Cat, and the chickens.

They were going down the Mississippi River in a houseboat.

192

A big, shivering, wet, yellow hound dog was standing there. "Woof!" The hound wagged his tail. He crossed the cabin to the stove. The dog lay down in a wet heap, flopped his tail three times against the cabin floor and fell asleep.

Jupiter crawled out from under the bed.

Gloriana still had her head under the sheet.

"Come out," said Jupiter. "It's only a dog."

Augustus went to the door and looked out.
A pile of wood drifted against the back deck.

"I guess there was a big flood," Augustus
said. "That hound dog must have drifted down
river on that pile of wood."

Tom Cat woke up and sniffed at the hound,
and then curled up beside him and went to
sleep.

The houseboat still drifted on down the
Mississippi.

There was no wind.

And the great river rolled along, still and
black. A star came out in the sky.

Augustus opened the cabin door and looked
outside. The river didn't look so strange, now
that the rain and the wind had stopped.

The houseboat seemed big and safe.

Jupiter was asleep.

"I'll keep watch," Augustus said. "I'll take that first lookout."

Gloriana nodded.

"No need to stand up," said Augustus, and he sat down on his bed where he could look through the cabin window.

The houseboat rocked through the night.

Cat and the hound dog were sound asleep.

On one side of the cabin Jupiter and Gloriana were sleeping too.

On the other side Augustus was keeping lookout—FAST asleep.

YUCCA

Yucca
Growing
So tall,
Like candles;
Like candles;
So white,
With a flower
For light.

We twist your little leaves
Into strings of thread;
We knot your strong stems
Into rope.
We weave your fibers
Into mats and baskets;
We pound your roots
For soap to make us clean.

Yucca,
Tall, white Yucca,
You make my heart sing
With your beauty.

Ann Nolan Clark

200

CHIPMUNK GOES HUNTING ➔

Long ago in the middle of a deep, dark forest, there lived an Indian boy. His name was Chipmunk.

Chipmunk lived with his father and mother and his little brother in a house made of logs and bark, near a big lake.

201

One morning he jumped out of bed and ran to the doorway to look out.

His mother was fixing breakfast over a fire outside the door. She smiled at him.

Today Chipmunk was going hunting with his Uncle, Many-Deer.

His Uncle, Many-Deer, was a chief of the village and a great hunter. It was an uncle's job to teach his sister's sons to hunt. And now Chipmunk was old enough to go with him— old enough to learn to track animals and to find his way in the deep woods—to learn to be a hunter.

Chipmunk's father was a great hunter too. He had made the small bow and arrows and the knife with its flint blade—the knife that Chipmunk would take with him into the woods.

Chipmunk knew he must learn to hunt. All the boys were glad when they were big enough to hunt.

One of his friends ran past on the way to the lake.

"You're going out with your uncle today," he called. "This will be a good day for you."

Chipmunk was very sad. For he had a secret. He was afraid—afraid of the forest.

He knew the paths near his village. He had often gone with the other boys a little way into the forest to hunt rabbits. But he was afraid in the deep woods. It was so still there.

Two or three times he had been sent into the woods at night to bring back water from the brook. That was to make a boy brave. But it hadn't made Chipmunk brave. Every leaf that moved and every branch that cracked made him afraid.

He didn't want his uncle to know about this. So Chipmunk kept his secret to himself.

Now he ate the breakfast that his mother gave him. Soon he saw his uncle coming across the village from his own house.

"Are you ready?" Many-Deer asked.

"I am ready," said Chipmunk, but he did not feel at all ready. And he was a little afraid of his uncle too. Many-Deer was so big, and he didn't smile.

They started out through the trees following a path that had been made by the feet of the hunters. Many-Deer went first, and then Chipmunk followed along.

It was still in the forest. He only heard the wind in the treetops, the call of the bird, and the bubbling of a brook.

"This brook runs into our lake," Many-Deer said. "It can help you find your way if you are lost."

"Yes, Uncle," said Chipmunk.

"See the knife marks on the trees beside the trail," said Many-Deer. "If you see these marks, you will know that one of our hunters made them. They will help you find your way, and you can make your own marks with your knife."

"Yes, Uncle," said Chipmunk again.

They walked on along the trail, away from the village, until they were in the deep woods, and Chipmunk hurried to keep up with his uncle.

207

At last they came to a place in the forest where the sunlight came through the trees.

"This is a good place to watch for deer," said Many-Deer. "They come here often. You stand in back of this tree, and I will go a little way off. Keep very still."

Many-Deer moved away. His feet made no noise on the soft ground. Soon he was gone.

Chipmunk could not see him.

Chipmunk stayed quietly by the tree. He listened and he watched.

Then something moved. It was only a little brown bird looking for bugs in the brush. Then there was another sound—a crashing sound. Something very big was coming. Was it a deer? No, it was too big for a deer. It must be a bear!

"Uncle," he shouted. "Where are you?" He shouted again. "Uncle!"

He began to run. The big animal ran too, and now he saw that it was a great stag. It bounded away into the forest.

Many-Deer was standing in the path. "You frightened the stag away!" he said. "Didn't I tell you to stand quietly? Why did you shout like that?"

"I thought it was a bear," said Chipmunk.

"A bear," said his uncle. "I would not have let a bear come near you. You knew I was watching close by. You have much to learn if you are going to be a hunter."

They went on into the forest, but they saw no more deer that day. At last they went back to the village.

Next morning, Many-Deer and Chipmunk started out again.

"Now remember, no shouting—no shouting today," said Many-Deer, "and do not run." He went first and Chipmunk followed.

"I mustn't be afraid. I mustn't be afraid," he said to himself.

He looked up at the great trees. He could not see the sky. He heard only the wind going "sh-sh-sh" in the treetops. Then something was over his head. It was a great bird. It moved through the trees without a sound.

Chipmunk was so frightened that he began to run. His feet cracked the branches and leaves on the ground and the bird was gone.

Many-Deer was standing still in the path when Chipmunk ran into him. He was very angry.

"Why do you do this?" Many-Deer asked. "I said that you were not to run."

"But that great big bird!" said Chipmunk. "It was flying over my head."

"That was an owl," said Many-Deer. "It was flying to its nest after a long night's hunting. You have frightened all the game in this part of the forest. Now we will have to go to another place. Remember to be like a hunter—not like a frightened rabbit."

"Yes, Uncle," said Chipmunk in a very small voice.

He followed his uncle along the trail. On and on they went, far into the forest. At last Chipmunk stopped to rest. But when he was ready to start again, he could not see his uncle. He looked for the trail, but he could not find it. There were trees on all sides, but he saw no knife marks on them.

He heard the sound of the brook, but the brook was far away, somewhere below him. He looked down and saw green leaves and green branches. The ground at his feet just dropped away. He was standing on the rim of a deep gorge. The gorge was so deep that he could look out over the tops of the trees that grew there. The brook was far down in the gorge.

He was alone in this strange still forest. He was lost!

"Uncle!" he shouted. "Where are you?"

He began to run. He pushed his way through the brush.

"I am here," said Many-Deer, "here in the path."

Why, his voice sounded very near! There was the trail, only a little way back from the gorge. Chipmunk waited there with his head down.

Many-Deer did not smile.

"You are not ready to be a hunter," he said. "Go back to the village and help your mother."

ONCE A FOREST

There's a whirring sound in the forest,

"Timber!" the voices call.

I hear the buzz of a busy saw

And the crack of trees that fall.

And now where once was a forest,

Are houses row on row.

I wonder about that forest.

Where did the animals go?

Patricia Miles Martin

215

NO, NO, ROSINA

Rosina's family had the most beautiful fishing boat in the fleet. And never once had she gone crab fishing with her father and her brothers and her uncle. NEVER once.

"Papa, can I go?" Rosina asked.

"You ask again!" Papa said. "The little one asks again."

"Your place is at home," Mama said.

"But when Luigi and Carlo are gone, I'm lonesome," Rosina said.

"Never mind," said Mama. "Next week you will all be back in school."

"But what about now?" Rosina asked.

"No, no, Rosina," said Luigi. "A fishing boat is no place for a girl."

"A woman on a fishing boat brings bad luck," Papa shouted.

"But she's such a small woman, maybe she won't bring bad luck at all," said Carlo.

While she ate her breakfast, Rosina thought about the talk of the morning. This time when she asked to go, Papa had not said no.
Not exactly.
Then Rosina knew what she must do.

She must show Papa that she wouldn't bring bad luck. She would go aboard the Santa Rosa and surprise him. She would hide on the Santa Rosa and show him that she wouldn't bring bad luck at all.

Papa and the brothers were still eating.

Rosina ran along the sidewalk down to the dock.

There in the morning fog the Santa Rosa waited, rocking against the ladder that led down from the dock.

Rosina went down the ladder. She went aboard, and she looked for a place to hide.

On deck was a big crab box, ready for the day's catch. And there inside the little cabin was an old coat hanging on a peg—almost as if it were waiting for Rosina. She hid inside the coat and waited.

Everyone on land was starting to go to work.

Men were calling to each other.

Then Papa and Rosina's brothers were coming down the ladder—and they were aboard. And Uncle came aboard too.

The Santa Rosa was leaving the dock—
heading for the Golden Gate. And then
it was chugging through the Golden Gate,
and on to find the yellow floats that marked
the place where their own crab pots lay deep
in the water.

"Here are our crab pots," Papa shouted.

"Lots of crabs," Luigi said.

This was the time for Rosina. "Guess who's here," she said.

"It's a little crab named Rosina," Luigi said.

Papa held his head. He was very angry.

"Papa," Rosina said. "I only wanted to show you that I wouldn't bring bad luck."

"I will talk to you later about this," Papa said. "Carlo, radio ashore and say to tell Mama that we have Rosina." He looked at Luigi. "Why do we stand here? We have work to do."

Luigi put the crabs in the wooden box. "They look small," he said.

"They are TOO small," said Uncle. "Not one is big enough to keep."

Uncle threw the little crabs into the sea. They chugged on to the next crab pot.

"Look," said Papa. "Not one is big enough to keep."

The third crab pot was filled.

"These look better," said Uncle.

All morning they worked. The big crabs went into the big crab box, and the little ones were dropped back into the sea.

"We have had good luck today," said Rosina.

Papa didn't answer.

Carlo spoke softly. "Look at the crabs, Papa. We have a good catch. Rosina did not bring bad luck."

When the fog cleared and the sun was high, they started for the Golden Gate.

Rosina knew that she could never again ask Papa to go on the Santa Rosa. This was one day she would remember. She would remember every bit of it. She waved at all the other fishing boats. She waved at people on land. And when they reached the dock, she was the last to go up the ladder.

223

At home Papa talked with Rosina. He talked for a long time. And then he said, "Now you will talk with Mama."

"I'm sorry," Rosina said to Mama. "I'll never go away again without telling you first."

The next morning Rosina called to her brothers.

"Rise and shine," Rosina said. "Hit the deck. Up, Luigi. Up. Carlo."

Again Rosina would be at home alone.

"Cheer up," said Carlo. "Luigi and I have to work at the dock today. And today Mama is going to let you go with Papa—one more time!"

Rosina was too happy to talk. She had NEVER been so happy. She put on Luigi's yellow coat. She borrowed Carlo's hat.

Papa was shouting.

"Fix a good lunch, Mama," he said, as he patted the top of Carlo's hat. "Fix a good lunch for me and my crew."

ANDY'S HIDE-OUT

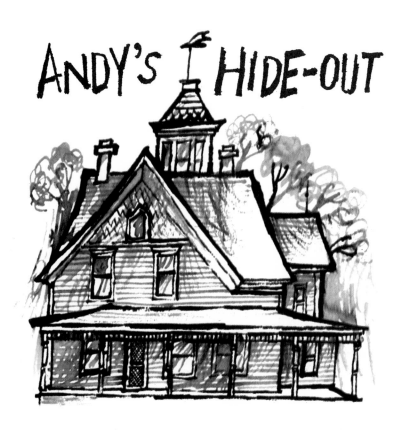

Andy and his mother and father, his twin sisters, Kate and Jill, and his grandmother had just moved into an old, old house.

In back there was a narrow yard with an old, old apple tree.

In the house were many small rooms—rooms with narrow windows. The twins had a room all their own. There was a place for everyone to sleep but Andy.

"I don't see where I'm going to sleep," he said.

"Well," said his grandmother. "We will have to decide about a place for you to sleep."

Everyone sat down to have a cup of soup for lunch. There was a paper at Andy's place. It had his name on it. He picked it up and read:

for Andy...
Where Does A Bird Fly?
Look And You Will Find A
Small Old House, And In
This House There Is
Something Just for You.

"It's a treasure hunt," said Andy. "And there's nothing I like better than a treasure hunt. And this is my first clue. It tells me where to hunt." He looked at his sisters. "Do you know about this ?"

The twins nodded.

"But we won't tell," said Jill.

226

"Do you know what the treasure is?" Andy asked them. The twins nodded again.

"I wonder what it is," Andy said. He looked all around. "Now where does a bird fly? Up."

So he went all around his own house and looked up at the roof, but there was nothing there. He went over to the apple tree, and he saw an old nest, high up in the green branches.

"Maybe that bird nest is what I'm looking for," Andy said. "A bird would fly there, and that old nest is a bird's house."

227

Andy climbed up and looked in the nest.

"There's a key here," Andy said. He reached into the nest and took out a golden key and a note. "This key is part of my treasure."

He climbed down from the tree with the paper in his teeth.

He read the note on the paper.

Where Does A House Mouse Go?
Look And You Will Find
A Golden Star ☆

"Where does a house mouse go?" Andy asked himself. "In a hole," he said.

"My key will fit a keyhole somewhere—I wonder where?"

Andy looked all through the house, and then, not far from the front door, he found a golden star. And in the star was a keyhole. So Andy put the key in the keyhole, and a narrow secret door opened.

229

And there were narrow steps that went around and around and up.

Andy went up first. The twins went next. The rest of the family followed. They went up and up and up.

And there at the very top of the house was his treasure—a little room, a very little room, with windows all around it.

Andy looked out over the top of the apple tree, over rooftops, and at the blue-gray sky above them.

"This is the best room in the house," he said.

He ran down the narrow steps, around and around, and he made a sign and put it under the golden star.

The End of the Treasure Hunt
ANDY'S HIDE-OUT

GRAND CANYON NATIONAL PARK

It was summertime.

Joey and his mother and father decided they would go to see one of our great parks.

They decided to go to the Grand Canyon National Park.

When they reached the park, Joey was the first one out of the car. There below him was the great gorge of the Grand Canyon National Park.

Far below were mountains and valleys, red and yellow, pink and brown, black and white.

231

232

PHOTO BY ESTHER HENDERSON

233

Joey saw a river winding—winding like a long gray snake.

"That river is one mile down," Father said.

They chose a place to make their camp.

Joey listened to people in camp talking about this National Park.

He heard one man say that squirrels and lizards and deer could be found in the canyon.

Another man was saying that once, long, long ago, there was a great sea here, and together, weather and time cut out this Grand Canyon.

The next morning Joey and his mother and father started walking down the trail. Joey watched for deer and lizards and squirrels.

Ahead were people on mules. But Joey and his mother and father walked because Joey could not ride a mule in the canyon. It would be a long time before he would be old enough to ride a mule down the narrow trail.

They walked a long time, and Joey looked at the river far down below, and he knew he would never get to the end of the trail.

"It is time for me to go back to camp," his mother said.

Joey didn't say it, but he knew it was time for HIM to go back too.

"I will come back some day," Joey thought, "and I will ride a mule along this trail."

On the way back up to camp a very small lizard slid under a rock. Two squirrels—two very fat squirrels—flipped their tails and frisked along the rim of the canyon.

That night they all sat around the camp fire. They saw pictures of deer and squirrels, lizards and snakes, and all the animals that live in the park. They watched the Indians dance their feather dance, and they all sat around and watched the fire burn low.

When they were ready to go home, Joey took one last look at the Grand Canyon—the beautiful gorge that lay below.

"I am glad we decided to come here," he said. "The Grand Canyon National Park is something I'll never forget."

What Is the Secret?

Read all the words and phrases in each group. Can you find how they are all alike?

1. boat   coat

   road   goat

   soap   roar

   foam   moan

   croak   roam

2. outside   a pounding

   a bounce   a round cloud

   flour   a house mouse

   pouting   loud sounds

   shouts   found a hound

How would *you* group these?

   knick knack   gladness

   glass   a knife

   gliding   knocking

   knowing   a glow

Make a list of things that are alike in some way. See if the others can guess your secret.

Can You Solve a Puzzle?

Make this on your paper.

1.	2.	3.	4.	5.	6.	7.	8.	9.	10.	11.

Write in each square on your paper only the first letter of the following words in the order given and you will have the name of someone in your family.

1. This is an animal with a long, long neck.

2. This is an animal with a mask on its face.

3. We can thank Johnny Appleseed for these.

4. You hear this when many boys play.

5. Stanley is one.

6. A cow gives this.

7. A kind of tree that a bear climbed.

8. Five and five make this.

9. In the summer the weather is this.

10. This is an animal with a trunk.

11. Some people carry an umbrella when it does this.

Tales
old &
New

6

MICE

I think mice
Are rather nice.

Their tails are long,
Their faces small,
They haven't any
Chins at all.
Their ears are pink,
Their teeth are white,
They run about
The house at night.
They nibble things
They shouldn't touch
And no one seems
To like them much.

But I think mice
Are nice.

Rose Fyleman

240

THE MEETING OF THE MICE

CHARACTERS

OLD MOUSE	BIRD
MIDDLE HOUSE MOUSE	BIG FIELD MOUSE
SMALL MOUSE	MIDDLE FIELD MOUSE
VERY SMALL MICE	LITTLE FIELD MOUSE
CAT	TINY FIELD MICE

ACT ONE

COMMENTATOR: All the little house mice live
under the stairs in a big white
house. Outside the hole, which
is the door to their house, is
a fat cat, waiting—waiting—

(The mice sit quietly under the stairs. Old Mouse
goes to the hole, looks through, and backs away.)

SMALL MOUSE: Did you see anything?
Anything at all?

OLD MOUSE: That cat is out there again.
She is sitting out there waiting.

SMALL MOUSE: What is she waiting for?

OLD MOUSE: She is waiting for US.

MIDDLE HOUSE MOUSE: She comes on soft feet. I wish
I could hear her when she comes.

SMALL MOUSE: I wish I could hear her when
she goes away.

MIDDLE HOUSE MOUSE: If she would ONLY bark like a
dog, THEN we would hear her.
We would know that SOMETHING
was out there.

SMALL MOUSE: If she would ONLY make a noise
like a cat, we would know
EXACTLY what was there.

VERY SMALL MICE: (*Softly*) THEN we'd know!

242

OLD MOUSE: Something must be done.
Something—

MIDDLE HOUSE MOUSE: Is there anything we can do?

SMALL MOUSE: Anything at all?

OLD MOUSE: I don't know. But I'll call a
meeting of the mice, and we can
decide what to do.

243

ACT TWO

COMMENTATOR: Outside the mouse house a bird flies here and there. He flies near the mouse house, chirping softly.

OLD MOUSE: (*From inside his house*) BIRD, BIRD, CAN YOU HEAR ME?

BIRD: (*Chirping*) I hear you, I hear you, Old Mouse.

OLD MOUSE: Will you do something for us?

BIRD: (*Chirping*) I'll do anything I can— anything I can—

OLD MOUSE: Will you please call a meeting of the mice? Will you ask them to meet us here tonight?

BIRD: (*Chirping*) Yes, I will—yes, I will—

244

COMMENTATOR: The bird flies away, and at
last he flies over a corn field
where little field mice
are eating corn.

BIRD: (*Bird is chirping as he flies
down, and the field mice stop
to listen.*)
I am calling the mice
to a meeting—to a meeting—
tonight—tonight—tonight.

BIG FIELD MOUSE: And where is the meeting to be,
Bird ?

BIRD: (*Chirping*) Under the stairs—
under the stairs—in the big house—
big house. (*He flies away.*)

ACT THREE

COMMENTATOR: Night comes and the cat lies down to sleep.

CAT: (*Cat goes to her bed and lies down to sleep.*) Purr—purr—purr—

(*The field mice creep into the big house and through the hole, into the mouse house. The mice sit together in a ring.*)

OLD MOUSE: There is a fat cat that sits outside our door every day.

MIDDLE FIELD MOUSE: WE know.

TINY LITTLE FIELD MICE: (*Softly*) We know—

LITTLE FIELD MOUSE: We know because that cat prowls in OUR field of corn.

BIG FIELD MOUSE: SOMETHING has to be done about that cat.

OLD MOUSE: That is exactly why I have called this meeting. We must decide what to do.

BIG FIELD MOUSE: I know exactly what to do. We must get a bell. If we have a bell, we can put it on the cat's neck. Any old bell will do. Any bell at all.

ALL MICE: HEAR—HEAR—

BIG FIELD MOUSE: It will be easy—VERY easy to find a bell somewhere in this big house.

ACT FOUR

COMMENTATOR: The mice look for the bell.

(Mice creep out through the hole.)

MIDDLE HOUSE MOUSE: There should be SOMETHING here in the kitchen.

LITTLE FIELD MOUSE: There is nothing here.

MIDDLE FIELD MOUSE: Not even a bit of corn.

MIDDLE HOUSE MOUSE: Not even a bite of cake.

LITTLE FIELD MOUSE: Not even any little seeds.

SMALL MOUSE: Not even a bit of bun.

BIG FIELD MOUSE: The bell ! The bell ! Let us not forget what we are looking for !

COMMENTATOR: The mice creep quietly up the stairs.

CAT:	Purr—purr—
BIG FIELD MOUSE:	What's THAT I hear ?
OLD HOUSE MOUSE:	It's the cat.
MIDDLE HOUSE MOUSE:	When we hear her purr, we know we're safe.
SMALL MOUSE:	Because she's asleep in her bed.
MIDDLE HOUSE MOUSE:	Maybe there is something in these boxes.

(The mice hunt through the boxes.)

SMALL MOUSE:	And there IS something ! See what I have found. Listen. *(He jingles a very little bell. Jingle jingle.)*
VERY SMALL MICE, *and* TINY FIELD MICE:	*(Softly)* A LITTLE bell !
BIG FIELD MOUSE:	That's a bell for a cat. It's exactly what we want.

COMMENTATOR: The mice go back down the stairs.

CAT: Purr—purr—purr—

BIG FIELD MOUSE: Hurry—hurry—

(The mice go through the hole and into the mouse house. They sit together in a ring.)

SMALL MOUSE: *(Jingles bell softly.)*

I have been thinking of something.

BIG FIELD MOUSE: This is a great thing !

MIDDLE FIELD MOUSE: Yes ! we have a bell for that cat.

SMALL MOUSE: May I say something ?

(He jingles the bell softly.)

BIG FIELD MOUSE: And I am the mouse who thought of finding the bell !

ALL MICE: HEAR—HEAR—

SMALL MOUSE: Please, may I ask something ?

OLD MOUSE: Ask anything you wish—

SMALL MOUSE: Who will put the bell on the cat?

ALL MICE: Not I !

Not I !

I won't !

I won't !

SMALL MOUSE: It makes ME afraid even to think about it.

OLD MOUSE: Then we can do nothing.

SMALL MOUSE: *(He softly jingles the bell.)*

It is easy to decide what to do—
But to do it—well, THAT'S not easy—not easy at all !

COMMENTATOR: All the mice nod, and because it is almost morning, the field mice hurry back to their field of corn, and the little house mice sit very still and listen for the cat.

251

THE GOBLIN

A goblin lives in our house, in our house, in
our house,
A goblin lives in our house all the year
round.
He bumps
And he jumps
And he thumps
And he stumps.
He knocks
And he rocks
And he rattles at the locks.
A goblin lives in our house, in our house, in
our house,
A goblin lives in our house all the year
round.

Rose Fyleman

252

HERE WE GO

Once there was a farmer who had a fine farm, fine horses and cows, a fine big house, and a fine wife and six children. He was a very happy man—happy, that is, but for one thing. There was a boggart in the house.

Boggart is the north-of-England name for a trick-playing spirit which moves into people's houses and barns and plays jokes on everyone.

This farmer had a boggart. The boggart would often walk around the house at night and take the sheets off of people. Sometimes it rapped on the door, and when the sleepy farmer got up, there would be no one there.

Often it would fall downstairs in the dark and make a great noise, and when the farmer's wife ran into the bedroom—afraid it was one of her children—all the children would be asleep in bed.

Sometimes it would just tap, tap, tap in the night. Sometimes it rolled a ball across the floor time and again, so no one could sleep. One night it threw all the pots and pans down the stairs.

Once in a while the boggart would help the family. It would wash the dishes when the farmer's wife wasn't looking. It would feed and water the horses and cows. But more often than not it would let them out, so the farmer had to go looking for them.

One of the things it liked to do was to blow the smoke back DOWN the chimney whenever anyone started to light a fire. Or it would blow out the flame just when someone wanted to make a light.

At last the farmer and his wife had enough of all this. Something had to be done.

So they decided to move. They decided to move to a new house on a big farm far away where there would be no boggarts.

The man and his wife and children packed up all their things and piled them high on the big wagon.

As they were about to drive off, a neighbor came by and said, "Oh, are you moving?"

"Yes," said the farmer. And he told his neighbor that they could not stand their boggart any longer, so they were moving.

So the neighbor wished them luck, and they drove off.

Then from the top of the load they heard a happy little voice say, "Well, here we go! We're off!"

THE MOUSE WHO LIKED TO READ IN BED

Scuffie was a little field mouse who liked to read in bed.

On a little night stand beside his bed was a pink birthday candle. The candle was his reading light.

Scuffie often chewed bits of paper and made them look like books.

One night his mother came in when he had just gone to bed and was ready to read.

"Scuffie," she said. "I don't think it is good for you to read so much in bed. And look at your candle. It has dripped down on your bed."

"Please let me read for a little while. I have all these books to read."

"All right," said his mother, "but don't read a long book. And don't forget to shut your outside door. You know why, don't you?"

"Yes, Mother, I know why," Scuffie said.

"You really should shut it right now," his mother said. And she gave him a small good-night mouse kiss.

When she was gone, Scuffie thought, "I really should get up and shut the door right now. I will do it in a little while."

He started to read. Then he heard something outside.

"What is that?" he thought.

It was his neighbors, Big Beetle and Little Beetle, who lived nearby.

"Hello," said Big Beetle. "I see that you are reading in bed."

"And with your door wide open," said Little Beetle. "You really should NOT do that, you know."

The beetles crawled away.

"I really should get up and shut the door right now," said Scuffie. "I will do it in a little while."

He started to read.

Then he heard a sound like a tail hitting the ground—thump—thump—thump—

He heard it again—thump—thump—

He looked up.

There was the cat.

"Oh my," Scuffie thought. "I should never have left my door open. It's too late to shut it now—"

"I see you," said the cat. "You are reading in bed."

Now Scuffie was very frightened. There was the cat, so big—so big—and there he was, just a little, little mouse—

But he said in a brave little voice, "Would you like to hear me read a story ? I will read a story to you if you would like to listen."

The cat looked at Scuffie. "I'll listen if you read a good cat story."

Scuffie began to make up a story.

His voice was high and frightened.

He read, "The people in this neighborhood are having a BIG day tomorrow. Tomorrow is going to be Cat Chasing Day. They will get umbrellas and sticks and run after cats. So all cats should go somewhere else right away, and stay away all day tomorrow. For tomorrow, Cat Chasing Day, will be a bad day for cats—"

Scuffie waited for the cat to say something, but the cat didn't say anything at all.

When Scuffie looked at the doorway, he had a great surprise. The cat had gone.

Scuffie got up and shut the door.

He had just popped into bed again when his mother and father came in.

"Scuffie," his mother said. "If you MUST read a story in bed, please read softly. You make too much noise."

"And now it is really time to put out your light," said his father.

As they left Scuffie heard his mother say, "I am glad he remembered to shut his door."

"I'll remember tomorrow," Scuffie said to himself. "I'll remember to shut it tomorrow and every night after this." He put out his candle and lay in his bed shivering.

Then he was very hungry. He remembered the pink candle that had dripped on his bed.

After he ate that off, he wasn't afraid any more, and he stopped shivering and fell asleep.

THE BEAR SAYS NORTH

One day while Osmo, the Bear, was prowling about the woods he caught a Grouse.

"Pretty good!" he thought to himself. "Wouldn't the other animals be surprised if they knew old Osmo had caught a Grouse!"

He was so proud of his feat that he wanted all the world to know of it. So, holding the Grouse carefully in his teeth without injuring it, he began parading up and down the forest ways.

"They'll all certainly envy me this nice plump Grouse," he thought. "And they won't be so ready to call me awkward and lumbering after this, either!"

264

Presently Mikko, the Fox, sauntered by. He saw at once that Osmo was showing off and he determined that the Bear would not get the satisfaction of any admiration from him. So he pretended not to see the Grouse at all. Instead he pointed his nose upwards and sniffed.

"Um! Um!" grunted Osmo, trying to attract attention to himself.

"Ah," Mikko remarked, casually, "is that you, Osmo? What way is the wind blowing to-day? Can you tell me?"

Osmo, of course, could not answer without opening his mouth, so he grunted again hoping that Mikko would have to notice why he couldn't answer. But the Fox didn't glance at him at all. With his nose still pointed upwards he kept sniffing the air.

"It seems to me it's from the South," he said. "Isn't it from the South, Osmo?"

"Um! Um! Um!" the Bear grunted.

"You say it is from the South, Osmo? Are you sure?"

"Um! Um!" Osmo repeated, growing every moment more impatient.

"Oh, not from the South, you say. Then from what direction is it blowing?"

By this time the Bear was so exasperated by Mikko's interest in the wind when he should have been admiring the Grouse that he forgot himself, opened his mouth, and roared out:

"North!"

Of course the instant he opened his mouth, the Grouse flew away.

"Now see what you've done!" he stormed angrily. "You've made me lose my fine plump Grouse!"

"I?" Mikko asked. "What had I to do with it?"

267

"You kept asking me about the wind until I opened my mouth—that's what you did!"

The Fox shrugged his shoulders.

"Why did you open your mouth?"

"Well, you can't say, 'North!' without opening your mouth, can you?" the Bear demanded.

The Fox laughed heartily.

"See here, Osmo, don't blame me. Blame yourself. If I had had that Grouse in my mouth and you had asked me about the wind, I should never have said, 'North!'"

"What would you have said?" the Bear asked.

Mikko, the rascal, laughed harder than ever. Then he clenched his teeth and said: "East!"

EAST

268

Old Tales

Some stories have been read by many people for a long, long time. Fables are one kind of old story. Some fables are as much as 2000 years old. Some may be older.

All fables are short. In most fables, instead of people talking, animals or objects speak. Most of the time in a fable only one important thing happens, and from what happens a lesson can be learned.

You know some fables. "The Hare and the Tortoise," and "The Ant and the Grasshopper" are the names of two that you may remember.

Here are pictures of two fables. If you don't know the story, can you make up one?

Old and New Ways of Saying Things

When things have been said the same way many times they lose their freshness. Stale sayings are called clichés. Can you think of some? Tell the missing word in these clichés.

1

High as a house

Quiet as a _____

2

Bold as brass

Clear as _____

3

White as a sheet

Red as a _____

4

Blue as the sky

Nice as _____

Now think of a new fresh way to say an old phrase. Instead of saying "hungry as a bear" you could say "hungry as a boy who has had nothing to eat for a year."

Try saying these in your own way.

Black as coal

White as a ghost

Warm as toast

Light as a feather

Fox and the Fire

Fox and the Fire

The young red fox stood near his cave on the side of a mountain.

For three days, a strange smell of danger had come with the wind. Now with the smell of danger, came the good smell of rabbit.

And the young red fox was hungry.

He started out to catch his supper.

He made no noise.

272

Close by, a gentle rabbit nibbled a weed.

The fox saw him and crept close.

Before the fox could catch his supper, a blue jay came low and screeched his anger, and the rabbit flashed into its burrow.

The fox whimpered, and sniffed at the burrow and scratched at the earth.

And even as he whimpered, gray-black smoke came heavy with the wind. Far away, in the forest, fire crawled along the ground and dry leaves snapped and crackled in its path.

The fox heard the roar of fire leaping from one tree to another, and he knew he must run.

273

At first he was bewildered and did not know which way to go.

Rabbits and mice came from their hiding places. Squirrels darted along the ground and quail called from the greasewood.

Two squirrels ran by and the fox followed behind them.

Sparrows and blue jays flew low overhead as the crackle of fire came closer.

Together, the animals ran out of the forest and the fox forgot that he was hungry.

On they went, across green fields until they came to a road.

The fox followed beside the road.

He came to a low brown house with a big tree growing beside it.

Beyond the tree was a barn.

Between the barn and the house was a pen, and inside the pen, a small chicken house.

With the strong, close smell of chicken came the smell of man and dog.

The fox shivered, ready to run, but there was no place to go.

275

Inside the house, a dog barked wildly, and the fox ran to the barn. Under the barn he found a small hole where he could hide.

He lay there——his nose on his paws——watching——

Rabbits and chipmunks, squirrels and mice, found hiding places. Squirrels and chipmunks went up in the tree, and rabbits and mice under the house.

Five deer came, and lay down close beside the barn.

276

The fox felt the shake of the earth when
the fire trucks rolled up, their red lights flashing
and their sirens screeching.

Cars came with men to help fight the fire.
With shovels and spades, they turned the
earth. Tanker trucks came and a fire fighting
bomber flew low overhead.

Inside the house, the dog howled like a wild
animal.

In the hours that followed, the fox huddled small in his hiding place.

The people at the ranch fought the fire with the fire fighters, and the fire was held back. The house, the barn, and the tree were saved.

When the fire was out, all the men went inside the house, and the fox remembered that he was hungry.

He crept from under the barn and went up to the house.

Through a window he saw a big black dog, walking back and forth.

He crept toward the road. When the earth was cool, he trotted back over the black fields.

The fox found his cave on the side of the mountain, but the leaves and grass were burned and the mountain was bare.

He hunted for his breakfast, but the rabbits and the mice had gone to new hiding places and the fox found nothing.

He hunted all day, and when night came, he started out across the black fields.

When he reached the ranch, he stopped. There was no sound from the low brown house.

The fox crept toward the chicken house.

With a mighty leap, the thin, hungry fox was over the fence.

Without making a sound, he went into the chicken house.

279

He reached up and seized a chicken. With one quick shake of his head, it was dead.

The chickens set up a great squawking, and the fox leaped up and over the fence and away.

The door to the house opened. People shouted and a dog barked. Then the dog came leaping through the doorway.

The fox ran toward the road.

He galloped along beside the fence.

The bark of the dog was close—closer—

The fox leaped to the top rail of the fence and waited there in the dark.

The dog did not see him,
and went racing by.

The fox went on along the top of the fence.
Far away, he could hear the bark of the dog.

Back in the barnyard, the dog trotted
around the chicken pen, and chickens scolded
softly and settled down again to sleep.

The fox did not return.

In the days that followed, seeds were planted in the burned earth, and clover and wild grass grew again.

In the forest, new branches grew green, and little animals found shelter in trees and in burrows.

282

The fox hunted for his supper.

And when he had eaten, he lay safe in his cave, and he cleaned his fur and pulled the burrs from between his toes.

When the moon rose low over the valley, he went outside and rolled in the dirt and shook himself.

He pointed his nose toward the moon and howled.

From far away, he heard a bark—a warning bark.

Far down in the valley, the black dog was answering his call.

The fox sniffed the air, and he smelled the good, cool, damp smell of green growing things, and trotted off into the forest.

285

· New Words in This Book ·

The following new words are presented in The Dog Next Door and Other Stories, Level Seven, Reading 360. Words printed in regular type are new basic words. Those underlined are enrichment words. Because of the large number of decodable words in this book they are not listed here. Decodable words for each selection are listed in the Teachers' Edition.

UNIT 1

Page

8	Bradleys		brush	38	worried	62	afraid
	move		again		until		enemies
	William		spell	40	across		eagle
	Lucy	18	hurried		showed		snake
	Brown		after	42	crawled	64	prowls
	door		washed	45	once	66	pronghorn
	doorway	20	left		floor		alone
9	two		prints	46	only		coyote
	moving	21	knew		exactly	69	stomach
	please		always	47	against		learn
	family		flipping		held	70	lies
10	front	23	rain		heard		flat
	by		umbrella	48	tail		ground
	Stanley	24	through		any		flashing
11	very	25	opened	50	puppy	71	herd
12	climbed		decided			73	beavers
	oak		proudly				drink
	higher	26	cloud		**UNIT 2**	74	young
13	almost	28	drop				chew
	does	29	won't	56	bear	75	danger
14	our		own		supper	77	above
15	garden	30	listened		forest	80	armloads
	better	32	hair		chipmunks		tunnels
16	paint		hurry		creeping	81	low
	patio	33	bicycle	57	crash	83	Sylvester
	tossing		barber	58	hungry		clear
17	swished		ahead		acorns		voice
		34	window		high	84	chickens
		35	chair	59	branch		corn
		37	gone		broke	85	slice

286

LIST OF ILLUSTRATORS

Tom Cooke

Murray Tinkelman

David M. McPhail

Ed Emberley

George Guzzi

Leo and Diane Dillon

Hans Zander

Earl Thollander

Arthur and Pauline Perry

Jane Teiko Oka

John Schoenherr

A B C D E F G H I J K   7 6 5 4 3 2   PRINTED IN THE U.S.A.